CW00591762

TALES FROM AN ERUPTION
POMPEII HERCULANEUM OPLONTIS

Naples, Museo Archeologico Nazionale
20th March – 31st August 2003

Brussels, Musées Royaux d'Art et d'Histoire
8th October 2003 – 8th February 2004

Under the patronage of Carlo Azeglio Ciampi, President of the Republic of Italy
Carlo Azeglio Ciampi

Ministero per i Beni e le Attività Culturali
Soprintendenza archeologica di Pompei

Regione Campania
Assessorato ai Beni Culturali

Regione Campania
> l'arte conta

TALES FROM AN ERUPTION
POMPEII HERCULANEUM OPLONTIS

GUIDE TO THE EXHIBITION

edited by
Pier Giovanni Guzzo

Electa

Cover
Corridor from the garden
of the Villa of the Papyri
at Herculaneum.
Naples, Museo Archeologico Nazionale.
Photograph by Mimmo Jodice

Overall coordination
Anna Civale
Tiziana Rocco

Graphic design
Dario Tagliabue

Page layout
Roberta Leone

Editorial coordination
Cristina Garbagna

Editor
Paula Billingsley

Technical coordination
Paolo Verri
Andrea Panozzo

Translation
Jo Wallace-Hadrill

Iconographical research and catalogue entries
Anna Civale (A. C.)
Tiziana Rocco (T. R.)

Photographs
Fotografica Foglia S.a.S. di Alfredo
e Pio Foglia
Archivio della Soprintendenza
archeologica di Pompei
Archivio della Soprintendenza per i Beni
Archeologici di Napoli e Caserta
Amministrazione Provinciale, Avellino
Archivio Fratelli Alinari, Firenze
Foto-Atelier Louis Held, Weimar
Foto Saporetti di Marcello Saporetti,
Milano
Tate Enterprises Ltd, Londra

An editorial realisation
by Mondadori Electa S.p.A., Milano

www.electaweb.it

Tales from an Eruption
Pompeii, Herculaneum, Oplontis

Naples, Museo Archeologico Nazionale
20th March – 31st August 2003

Sponsoring institutions

Ministero per i Beni e le Attività Culturali

Regione Campania
Assessorato ai Beni Culturali

Soprintendenza per i Beni e le Attività Culturali della Regione Campania

Soprintendenza archeologica di Pompei

Soprintendenza per i Beni Archeologici di Napoli e Caserta

Advisory committee
Mariarosaria Borriello
Antonio d'Ambrosio
Stefano De Caro
Teresa Giove
Pier Giovanni Guzzo
Marisa Mastroroberto
Fausto Zevi

Coordination committee
Mariarosaria Borriello
Antonio d'Ambrosio
Marisa Mastroroberto

Exhibition curators
Antonio d'Ambrosio
Pier Giovanni Guzzo
Marisa Mastroroberto

Committee of Honour

On. Giuliano Urbani
Ministro per i Beni e le Attività Culturali

On. Antonio Bassolino
Presidente della Regione Campania

On. Marco Di Lello
Assessore ai Beni Culturali

Alessandro Porzio
Staff Director

Stefano De Caro
Soprintendente per i Beni e le Attività Culturali della Regione Campania

Pietro Giovanni Guzzo
Soprintendente archeologo di Pompei

Giovanni Lombardi
Direttore amministrativo della Soprintendenza archeologica di Pompei

Fausto Zevi
Soprintendente per i Beni Archeologici di Napoli e Caserta

Loaning instutions
Amministrazione Provinciale, Avellino
Civiche Raccolte d'Arte, Milano
Galleria d'Arte Moderna di Palazzo Pitti, Firenze
Kunstsammlungen zu Weimar
Museo di Storia della Fotografia Fratelli Alinari, Firenze
Museo e Gallerie Nazionali di Capodimonte, Napoli
Museo Nazionale di San Martino, Napoli
National Gallery of Scotland, Edimburgo

Organisation and press office
Mondadori Electa S.p.A.

Technical/organisational coordination
Anna Civale
Tiziana Rocco

Press office
Tiziana Benini
Ministero per i Beni e le Attività Culturali

Ilaria Maggi
Electa, Milan

Francesca De Lucia and Raffaella Levèque, Soprintendenza archeologica di Pompei

Exhibit design
Studio MetaImago/Rome
Maurizio di Puolo and Caterina Niccolini

Exhibition set-up and organisation
Meloni Fabrizio S.r.l., Rome
with Enrico Vandelli

Graphic design
Dario and Fabio Zannier

Information panels
Mondadori Electa S.p.A.
Anna Civale, Tiziana Rocco

Multi-vision programme
Wild Projection Studio di Ernani Paterra, Rome

Audio-visual apparatus and lights
Roseto Music Service, Davide Claps

Transport
Arteria S.r.l. - Divisione Propileo, Rome

Insurance
GENERALI
Assicurazioni Generali S.p.A.

The exhibition has been sponsored by

with the support of

and with the assistance of

Contents

Pier Giovanni Guzzo Tales from an Eruption

To confront Pompeii, even for a simple visit, means taking a decision in advance. It is a matter of chosing exactly what to see and is based on one's time and energy.
It is not only the vastness of the city that imposes this advance planning. The unexpected burial of the area around Vesuvius has conserved, with varying levels of clarity, extremely diverse categories of evidence.
In the ancient Vesuvian sites – unlike many others of different historical and cultural significance – the information available to archaeologists here ranges from nature to history. The definition of the former term is obviously broad, including not only geomorphological details (which are available at any ancient site) but also organic data, be it 'natural', in that it developed without human intervention, be it the result of human activity. So, from crop-farming to stock-raising, from the use of organic materials for various purposes to paleo-anthropological research, a vast and interesting field opens up: although not confined to the area affected by the eruption of 79 A.D., it is particularly abundant and well preserved there.
The evidence deriving from human activity contributes to historical knowledge: from the humblest finds of everyday objects to rich treasures, from a single building (composed of innumerable parts) to the city itself, globally interpreted, with regard to the organisation of production in an area spreading concentrically, from agricultural suburbs to exotic India (whence comes the ivory statue at the National Archaeological Museum of Naples). Even in terms of historical knowledge, what happened at the foot of Vesuvius is also known in other sites investigated by archaeologists, but, here too, the quantitative element is overwhelming. And it is multiplied when one recalls that human life in this area dates at least as far back as the second millennium, so that the quantity of surviving evidence takes on a millennial density.
In an attempt to reorganise the evidence, and thus create a matrix for the current acquisitions for the institutional purposes of the Soprintendenza, the two principal categories of time and space are adopted.
'Time' is defined roughly as the period from the eighteenth century to today; and 'space' by the area affected by the eruption.
Thus, in accordance with the Soprintendenza ai Beni Archeologici of Naples and Caserta, the period of discovery, already documented by Giuseppe Fiorelli in his *Pompeianorum Antiquitatum Historia,* is recorded with greater detail with references to the contemporary conditions of the movable and immovable objects which were found.
Today, space can be described with millimetrical precision, and computer technology allows us to turn a geometrically fixed point, into a file, so that all the information on the same point is organised and available for consultation. That is how a topographical map

of Pompeii was constructed, and work is in progress to do the same for Herculaneum.

But the web we are weaving offers different principles of organisation: one promises, for instance, to reinvestigate the ways of dealing with new finds and spreading knowledge about Pompeii. Another has to do with traditional typology of classes of production and activity; and yet another, with the traditional classification, typical of diachronic archaeology, of presenting information through the operation of excavations.

The usual categories that apply to protecting the cultural heritage of Italy, which reaches a high level here, are inadequate for these solid examples which hint at the vast possibilities of Vesuvian archaeology. Moreover, there is the matter of public consumption, the trigger for a fruitful production as yet not fully analysed, which one can tell at a glance involves both legal and illegal things.

Yet if one wished to devise a method to learn about Pompeii, a businesslike approach would not be entirely inappropriate.

The organisation of a worthwhile visit for a specific audience requires expertise and an ability to communicate and keep the visitors' attention so that they can absorb and remember the facts; thus it is essential to choose the right things to convey.

This approach could also be supported by the presence of a bookshop or coffee shop, as well as the illumination of some of the site (but which parts and how to do it?), without going so far as to actually restore the structure and decoration of the ancient monuments. But experience has shown that we are far from such an approach. At the most one can act as an intermediary, though commercial considerations are always uppermost. In a vision of the world which owes much to the Saturnalia one should consider the long-term objective and not daily concerns.

And nothing else can be expected from an age that seems more concerned with instant gratification through modern technology rather than the critical faculties of memory for extracting the best even through today's technology. Even if we were to take the analysis further, the results would always be confined to the ever-dwindling group of experts: when we use as we must the cold logic of choice, the bright flash of emotion or intuition is far more important.

But when dealing with people outside the charmed circle of archaeological erudition, a strategic position has to be taken along the lines discussed above. They – the non-experts – are far more numerous than we, and it is they who dictate public opinion and thus influence decisions *erga omnes*.

So when talking to laymen, one must indicate the reasons guiding the 'experts'' actions. And by illustrating the results achieved and the way to achieve them, one comes to realise that a long and methodical effort is necessary before the research be considered complete. The magic of ancient things coming to light, returning to mankind after a thousand or more years of sleep, too often turns archaeology into a Sleeping Beauty, a comprehensible attitude since everything really does seem to come to life again in the mysterious fascination of (re)discovery. Certainly, school is not much help, in the arduous task of distinguishing between magic and science, particularly recently, nor is the much-worshipped computer, that ubiquitous sorcerer's apprentice of our day, which we demand services from without understanding how they are performed.

Exhibitions are one of the main ways to promote dialogue between experts and public. These temporary displays, if well publicised, can command large numbers of visitors. The messages conveyed can be varied, as can the results. One could discuss at length what makes an exhibition successful for a museum. Timing and location are essential, even if young Holden who was so stressed by modern life went to a museum to relax. Thus experts must present their material in a manner comprehensible to the layman, without compromising their own level of scholarship. They do this at the risk of being marginalised from everyday life, considered magicians more than people doing the important job of preserving the past.

In our case, among the many ways of presenting the infinite amount of material from the eruption, is to focus on the almost two thousand bodies that were found, our ancestors identifiable as those people killed by the sudden violence of the eruption.

Too often the ancient world is presented as a sort of archetypal model: a sort of fixed, unmodifiable reality, which is displayed to our amazed admiration and allows for no explanations or comments.

In the ancient cities of Vesuvius, and particularly in Pompeii (including the many Herculaneans who died in the arcades along the beach), the bodies which were found, far from their own houses, in flight and no longer intent on daily tasks, help us to see the ancient world into a human light. Even the wonderful monuments of Athens and Rome, which are to be admired with religious awe, even when not understood, were built and used by ordinary men and women, however nothing material survives of these people and they speak to us solely through their achievements. But this is not the case at Pompeii, Herculaneum or Oplontis: these excavation sites, which are not so very dissimilar to others, are set apart because their sudden destruction preserved so many material remains of their inhabitants. These are the remains of the people who built the city, who lived in it and enjoyed it until the volcano put an end to their lives, their joy and their work.

And while the ancient Greeks, Romans, Egyptians and Carthaginians have been brought back to life by the imagination of writers, there

is no need here under Vesuvius to be a Verri or a Flaubert to understand the past. Any person of feeling can breathe life into those motionless shapes made by the bodies of those who suffocated and perished in the eruption.
In this exhibition, the underlying theme is the result of specialised research. Some is well documented, while other parts, for various reasons, are based upon hypotheses, albeit plausible ones. Nevertheless, this specialised research has produced impeccable results. It is possible to add details in the realm of archaeology without becoming involved in unneccessary scientific explanations, that make for a more immediate connection with 'non-experts'. These refer to the 'tales' about the people of ancient Pompeii, Herculaneum and Oplontis, whose bodies have been discovered and a description of what must have happened just before their deaths.
Through these figures, who have been dead for two thousand years, we can bring to life those frescoes, decorations, utensils, coins and jewels belonging to our collective imagination of Pompeii, which are frequently viewed out of context, and away from those who made and used them.
The act of comparing these ancient human bodies with our own ones will, we hope, spark off an interest which will continue to grow, fed by an informed desire to present not only objects but also 'tales'. These glimpses of life in the ancient world must be compared to our own ones in order to appreciate the differences, evaluate the distance which separates us, and realise that we too are people with both a past and a future.
The content of these 'tales' is not invented; it stems from a patient application of knowledge and interpretation, and is all based on fact. The experiment becomes scientific when one finds the same facts everywhere and in all cases, and obtains the same result.
We would be proud if those who visit this exhibition receive the impression that none of the exhibits have been put there by chance or even worse, by mistake, and I hope that this impression is given by the ample research documented in this volume.
If we achieve our desired end, one of the most interesting consequences will be the demystification of the magical art of archaeology. Certainly, the strong feelings inevitably evoked by archaeological discoveries will remain the same for we, experts, are also subject to these.
But if archaeology manages to (re)gain a scientifically disciplined role, maybe it should be more freely handed over to specialised technicians, rather than to people who organise events and fashion shows, run cafés, restaurants and shops, to improbable experts in other fields of study, or to financial wizards with their own kind of magic. Archaeology, when conducted along scientific lines, does not bear fruit of a financial kind, but it does serve to develop people's critical consciousness,

by allowing them to understand the history and achievements of mankind and not just the history of concepts, of illustrated deeds, of dates and battles.
It certainly never occurred to the ancient Pompeians that their lives and their actions would be the subject of historical reflection for so many centuries.

Eric M. Moormann   Literary Evocations of Ancient Pompeii

There are echoes of Pompeii in the literature of many countries. The Americans have a very long, though certainly forgotten poem – a hundred and eighty pages long – entitled *The Last Night of Pompeii*, written by Sumner Lincoln Fairfield in 1832, but also the diaries of travellers such as Herman Melville and Mark Twain (see below). In England there was the greatly renowned Edward George Bulwer-Lytton with *The Last Days of Pompeii*, published in 1835, though he was accused of plagiary by the aforementioned Fairfield. A century later we find Malcom Lowry's *Present Estate of Pompeii* of 1948, one of a collection of short stories entitled *Hear Us, O Lord, from Heaven Thy Dwelling Place* (1961, pp. 175–200), which describes the feelings of the Canadian Roderick McGregor Fairhaven when he visits Pompeii with his wife. Nobody in Germany has ever heard of Wilhelm Jensen, but many people know *Gradiva* (1903) thanks to the psychoanalysis of Sigmund Freud (1912).
In addition, there are various nineteenth-century novels, such as the verse epic *Euphorion* of Ferdinand Gregorovius of 1858. A few years ago, the Belgian writer Amélie Nothomb published *Peplum* (1996) in the popular series "Livres de poche", a work of science-fiction in which Pompeii is excavated again in the twentysixth century. The well-known Dutch archaeologist Frédéric-Louis Bastet writes both poetry and prose, among which is the story of an archaeologist who pushes his wife down a Pompeian well to get rid of her (*Lobster cocktail en andere verhalen,* 1986). France has a rich tradition of Pompeian literature: starting from the *Voyage du jeune Anacharsis en Grèce* of Abbot Barthélemy (1788) – one of the earliest examples of Pompeian literature known to me – we move on by way of Germaine de Staël's *Corinne* (1807) and Théophile Gautier's *Arria Marcella* (1852) to Jean Bertheroy's *La Danseuse de Pompéi* (1899) and more recent examples to which I will return later. The French archaeologist Pierre Gusman wrote a novel as well entitled *Elskée. Au jardin de Vénus (Souvenirs de Pompéi). Hexaméron polychrome* (1936), which tells the tale of a Danish girl who falls in love with the excavations and the people of the Vesuvian area. In Italy there are, among others, Leopardi with his long poem *La ginestra*, and with his political poem *Paralipomeni della Batracomiomachia* and, only twenty years ago, Primo Levi with two powerful poems in which Pompeii plays an important role (see below). In addition there are a children's story about Libero D'Orsi, the excavator of Stabia (*Carla degli scavi* by Renée Reggiani, 1968), and other examples which we will look at later.
Up till now, few people have tried to make sense of these works and others like them. Wolfgang Leppmann, Jean Seznec, Tomas Mikocky and Felix Fernández Murga have assembled much material and examined it, often from their own national or linguistic point of view. Claude Aziza has provided us with a rich anthology of French literary texts and some translations into French.[1]

The End of Pompeii

Pompeii has a double significance: it does not only represent a society which was wiped off the face of the earth in an instant by the intervention of the gods – either because of its decadence or through purely natural causes – but also

the resurrection of ancient culture. Sir Walter Scott called it the "City of Dead", although, it must be said, he was not much interested in the ancient world. "Cette momie de ville" is how Alexandre Dumas describes it, regarding Pompeian archaeology as an almost surgical process, or like the unwinding of bandages from a body in the hope of finding it almost entire after a sleep of so many centuries. James Fenimore Cooper used this image in his *Excursions in Italy,* 1838. Corinne and Oswald, in *Corinne* want to "pénétrer dans le passé". Charles Dickens (*Pictures from Italy*, 1846, in the chapter about Naples entitled *A Rapid Diorama*, Penguin ed., 1998, p. 169) looks towards Vesuvius and finds himself "in the strange and melancholy sensation of seeing the Destroyed and the Destroyer making this quiet picture in the sun."
The aforementioned poem by Leopardi, *La ginestra o il fiore del deserto,* is very well known, as far as Italy is concerned, and was published after the poet's death in 1845. During the years 1833–37, when he lived in Naples with his friend Ranieri, Leopardi made frequent long visits to Villa Ferigni, a property belonging to Ranieri's brother-in-law near Torre del Greco, from which he climbed Mount Vesuvius several times and went down from there to visit the excavations of Herculaneum and Pompeii, as Ranieri records in Leopardi's collection of poems which he edited (*I canti*, Firenze 1845).
Canto XXXIV was written at Torre del Greco in 1836. It is not a factual description, but an allusion to the devastating forces of Nature. Vesuvius gives the inspiration for a long digression on the human condition.

Detail from the cast of the so-called 'pregnant woman', found on the Via Stabiana

Cast of a man, found on the staircase of the House of Fabius Rufus at Pompeii

"Qui su l'arida schiena / del formidabil monte / sterminator Vesevo, / la qual null'altro allegra arbor né fiore, / tuoi cespi solitari intorno spargi, / odorata ginestra, / contenta dei deserti." [1–7]

"Questi campi cosparsi / di ceneri infeconde, e ricoperti / dell'impietrata lava, / che sotto i passi al peregrin risona; / dove s'annida e si contorce al sole / la serpe, e dove al noto / cavernoso covil torna il coniglio; / fur liete ville e colti, / e biondeggiàr di spiche, e risonaro / di muggito d'armenti; / fur giardini e palagi, / agli ozi de' potenti / gradito ospizio; e fur città famose / che coi torrenti suoi l'altero monte / dall'ignea bocca fulminando oppresse / con gli abitanti insieme. Or tutto intorno / una ruina involve." [17–33]

The Cause of the Destruction

Many people have asked themselves why the cataclysm struck these little towns in the foothills of Vesuvius. Were they without any political or economic importance in themselves, and therefore innocent, or were they guilty of something? The anonymous American author (Thomas Gray?) of *The Vestal of Pompeii* (1832), Fairfield and Bulwer-Lytton have a ready answer: Pompeii is validated as a symbol of the "decline and fall of the Roman empire". Not having instantly recognised the Truth which Christ revealed, apparently cost them their lives. This theory, as it would seem, also holds good for Massimo D'Azeglio, as he writes in his *Ricordi* (in *Opere varie*, 1966, p. 417), thinking back

to his youthful verses: "After writing the tercets, I had the idea of composing a romantic-archaeological poem with its action set in Pompeii, and its climax at its destruction. In the dead of night the avenging angel summoned up the demon of Vesuvius and pointed out to him the city which is condemned to destruction. I can't remember the precise reason, but as usual, it's along the lines of the corruption of the age. At the voice of the angel, the spectre of destruction rose from the crater, revealing himself from the waist upwards like Farinata, one hand forking up lava with his hellish pitchfork, while with the other he scatters ash on the condemned city. This would be the introduction. The main theme of the story would be filial love. A Roman soldier wants to free his mother, who is a slave. In the circus, a sum of money, enough to buy her freedom, has been promised to anyone who can beat a famous gladiator. The son leaves his cohort, disguises himself, beats his opponent, receives the prize, and frees his mother! But he is discovered and his centurion throws him into chains, with a view to bringing him to trial. His mother, at his side, comforts and embraces him and promises him his freedom after this brief punishment. Meanwhile, it is night and in the distance, a dull crash is heard, growing louder and mixing with screams and shouts. The ground quakes beneath their feet, the walls shake, a blood-red glow lights up the sky, thunder crashes, and then all hell breaks loose from on high, shattering, knocking down and burying the city. The poor mother, free herself, is urged by her son to flee; she would like to release him, but the shackles are too large and all hope is lost etc etc. As you can easily imagine, with this plot one could make a real packet … but I haven't written the poem yet."

In Bulwer-Lytton, the poor early Christians are considered pure Christians of the highest degree, that is to say not those of 'our own' times, but those who followed the apostles to the letter. I won't elaborate upon a hidden polemic here against the doctrine of the Church of England which teaches that, however important the Christian element, it is not the dominant theme.

In the book, the cult of Isis predominates, representing the foreigner who penetrates our culture and destroys it. Arbaces, the priest of Isis, represents the Orient, one of the evils to be feared. The image of the menacing Oriental becomes a cliché, and brings to mind the German archaeologist Johannes Overbeck and his *Pompeji in seinen Gebäuden, Alterthümern und Kunstwerken für Kunst- und Alterthumsfreunde dargestellt* (1856, p. 28; 1865, p. 31; 1875, p. 27; missing from the 1884 edition). When he recounts that a "fresh" offering has been found in the temple of Isis, he concludes "dass der neueste, fremdeste und abstruseste Aberglauben des sinkenden Heidenthums der zäheste gewesen sei."

Most of nineteenth century novels and short stories on this theme follow the pattern sketched by D'Azeglio and used by Bulwer-Lytton, with Jews and/or Christians against the pagans, who are snuffed out by the eruption of Vesuvius. Fixed elements in such texts are secret meetings between members of the sect, law-court scenes in which the victims are condemned, gladiatorial games in the amphitheatre and the eruption of the volcano which puts an end to all of it. There is a glut of such novels and short stories at the end of the nineteenth and the beginning of the twentieth century. Some titles are worth a mention: Comtesse de Bassanville, *La maison maudite. Nouvelle pompéienne* (in *Nouvelles cosmopolites. Mœurs, coutumes de divers peuples de l'Europe*, n.d. [*c.* 1880], pp. 248–334); Emily Sarah Holt, *The Slave Girl of Pompeii* (n.d. [*c.* 1886]); Woldemar Kaden, *In der Morgenröthe* (in *Pompejanische Novellen und andere*, 1892, pp. 1–228); Gustav Adolf Müller, *Das sterbende Pompeji. Ein Roman aus Pompejis letzten Tagen* (1910). In a novel written by the Italian doctor Oscar Rosoni, *Amore e morte a Pompei* (1970), Jews and Christians are depicted with a heavily anti-semitic slant. The Jewish main character loses his life at the same moment and for the same reason as the pagan Pompeians, that of not accepting the Christian faith. The writer's profession is evident on every page, with digressions on ancient diet and healthcare, and on diseases and accidents.

Death in Pompeii: the Victims

Guidebooks, handbooks and literary works all touch our hearts with feelings and emotion when they describe the remains of the human beings: the skeletons, the imprints of people in the layers of lapilli and ash, and the truly dramatic plaster casts that were made from 1860 onwards, using a technique introduced by Giuseppe Fiorelli. The guides knew how to (and probably still do) tell little tales which would make their clients shudder. The idea of the Gothic novel, the stories with spirits and the returning dead, became very popular at the end of the eighteenth and in the nineteenth century. The following are among the most famous titles (and are all from authors who visited Herculaneum and/or Pompeii): *The Castle of Otranto* by Horace Walpole, 1764; *Vathek* by William Beckford,1786; *Frankenstein* by Mary Shelley Wollstonecraft, 1818; the novels of Walter Scott and the operas inspired by him, as well as *The Marble Faun* by Nathaniel Hawthorne,1860; and *Dracula* by Bram Stoker, 1897. Such works, which do not present easy points of comparison among themselves, are linked by an attraction for death and the irrational.

Le diable amoureux. Nouvelle espagnole by Jacques Cazotte (1772) begins in a grotto at Herculaneum: the Spanish official Don Alvare Maravillas meets the devil, first in the form of a dog and then in the incarnation of the beautiful Biondetta. Their adventures take place in Venice and in Spain, but everything is initiated in the "ruines de Portici ... Ces restes des monuments les plus augustes, écroulés, brisés, épars, couverts de ronces, portent à mon imagination des idées qui ne m'étaient pas ordinaires."

The Last Days of Pompeii by Bulwer-Lytton, *Arria Marcella* by Gautier and, a few decades later, Jensen's *Gradiva* (which has the significant subtitle of *Ein pompejanisches Phantasiestück*) belong to a worthy tradition of evoking the victims of Pompeii.

A perhaps unexpected evocation is that which comes from Primo Levi in *Ad ora incerta* (1984). In *La bambina di Pompei* Levi sees a Pompeian cast in an historical vision, along with Anne Frank and an anoymous victim of Hiroshima: the Second World War is a cataclysm which killed innocent people, similar to that of Pompeii, but caused by men and not by a volcano. "La bambina di Pompei / Poiché l'angoscia di ciascuno è la nostra / Ancora riviviamo la tua, fanciulla scarna / Che ti sei stretta convulsamente a tua madre / Quasi volessi ripenetrare in lei / Quando al meriggio il cielo si è fatto nero. / Invano, perché l'aria volta in veleno / È filtrata a cercarti per le finestre serrate / Della tua casa tranquilla dalle robuste pareti / Lieta già del tuo canto e del tuo timido riso. / Sono passati i secoli, la cenere si è pietrificata / A incarcerare per sempre codeste membra gentili. / Così tu rimani tra noi, contorto calco di gesso, / Agonia senza fine, terribile testimonianza / Di quanto importi agli dei l'orgoglioso nostro seme. / Ma nulla rimane fra noi della tua lontana sorella, / Della fanciulla d'Olanda murata fra quattro mura / Che pure scrisse la sua giovinezza senza domani: / La sua cenere muta è stata dispersa dal vento, / La sua breve vita rinchiusa in un quaderno sgualcito. / Nulla rimane della scolara di Hiroshima, / Ombra confitta nel muro dalla luce di mille soli, / Vittima sacrificata sull'altare della paura. / Potenti della terra padroni di nuovi veleni, / Tristi custodi segreti del tuono definitivo, / Ci bastano d'assai le afflizioni donate dal cielo. / Prima di premere il dito, fermatevi e considerate (20 novembre 1978)."

Detail from the cast of a child found under the stairs in the House of the Golden Bracelet at Pompeii

Was There Really a Sentry?

One of the stories which is frequently told, and certainly more entertaining than the aforementioned verses, has as its subject a supposed sentry at the Vesuvius Gate. The area of the tombs and the Villa of Diomedes takes up a lot of space in descriptions of their discovery, dating from 1760 onwards. I refer, more precisely, to a structure with a rectangular niche on the left immediately outside the gate.[2]

Let us begin with an excerpt from *The Innocents Abroad* (1869, chapter 31, anastatic ed. 1996, pp. 327–336), a witty account of a journey to Europe and the East by Mark Twain. Twain, in the guise of a journalist, visits Pompeii in 1867 and recounts (p. 335): "But perhaps the most poetical thing Pompeii has yielded to modern research was that grand figure of a Roman soldier clad in complete armor; who, true to his duty, true to his proud name of a soldier of Rome, and full of the stern courage which had given to that name its glory, stood to his post by the city gate, erect and unflinching, till the hell that raged around him burned out the dauntless spirit it could not conquer.

We never read of Pompeii but we think of that soldier; we cannot write of Pompeii without the natural impulse to grant to him the mention he so well deserves. Let us remember that he was a soldier – not a policeman – and so, praise him. Being a soldier, he staid, – because the warrior instinct forbade him to fly. Had he been a policeman he would have staid, also – because he would have been asleep."

Where did Twain get this story from? Is it a simple whimsical invention of his own, or a serious idea which he got from a guidebook? Let us proceed

in chronological order and begin with the earliest bit of written evidence, that of the original excavation of the small building, which Twain certainly did not consult. In 1763 Karl Weber did indeed write in his excavation diary (G. Fiorelli, *Pompeianarum Antiquitatum Historia,* I, 1860, pp. 152–153): "13 Agosto – En el mismo lugar se descubrió una fuente de mármol blanco 4 pal. larga. Además de una sede de piperno dulce sin inscripción, se descubrió una capilla a bóveda y dos inscripciones en ella, una de mármol blanco de 6 pal. y 7 on. por 2 pal. con 2 cuervos escolpidos abajo, y sobre la misma inscripción de cerca 6 on. y debajo de dicha inscripción hay un nicho adorno de mármol blanco y cornís alto pal. 4 y 9 on. y muy estrecho cerca 7 on., y adentro está la pedaña de alguna estatua que ahora no existe; la otra inscripción está en el pedestal de travertino en el medio de la capilla, alto 2 pal. y 6 on. y de 1 pal. y 5 on. en cuadro. Y tanto la una que la otra inscripción es del tenor siguiente: m. cerrinivs / restitvtvs / avgvstalis / loc. d. d. d."

Johann Joachim Winckelmann cites this discovery in *Nachrichten von den neuesten Herculanischen Entdeckungen* (1764, pp. 20–21; 1997 ed., eds. S.G. Bruer and M. Kunze, p. 19) and describes the tomb briefly; he has got his information directly from Weber. A decade or so later, Mariana Starke, who visited the site in 1798, gives a different interpretation of it and writes in *Travels in Italy between the Years 1792 and 1798* (1802, II, p. 105): "The City-Gate is highly interesting; here is the sentry-box for the Guard."

Sir William Gell, one of the people who knew Pompeii best at the beginning of the nineteenth century, published *Pompeiana* in 1819, which for decades remained one of the most authoritative description of the site, not only among the English. Many travellers paint a sympathetic portrait of this gentleman who was always so willing to give information about the excavations.

He describes the monument near the Herculaneum Gate in 1819 as follows (III ed. 1852, p. 63): "An arched recess, around and without which seats are formed … Within this recess was found a human skeleton, of which the hand still grasped a lance. Conjecture has imagined this the remains of a sentinel, who preferred dying on his post to quitting it for the more ignominious death, which, in conformity with the severe discipline of his country, would have awaited him."

For another Pompeian expert, the French architect François Mazois (*Les ruïnes de Pompéi*, I, 1824, pp. 27–28), the building is rather "consacré sans doute à quelqu'une de ces divinités qui président aux chemins, et que les anciens appelaient Viales dii: il était orné de peintures aujourd'hui détruites. Dans la niche du fond on avait représenté la figure de la divinité, et en face était une pierre cubique qui servait d'autel pour y déposer des fleurs, des fruits, brûler des parfums, ou sacrifier de petits oiseaux."

The countess of Blessington visited Pompeii several times, as she notes in *The Idler in Italy* (1839). At the beginning of September 1823 she is at the site with Gell, who no doubt tells her the story (p. 276): "On the right is an arched alcove, round which is a bench of marble. An altar, with a very beautiful bronze tripod, stood in the centre (and are now in the Museum), and this gave rise to the supposition that the alcove was dedicated to some sylvan deity. To me it appeared rightly as a reposoir, erected for the convenience of persons to wait in until the gate was opened, as it stands very close to it ... A skeleton, with a spear still grasped in its hand, was found in the reposoir, and is supposed to have been that of a sentinel, who met death at his post, the spear held even in dead attesting his constancy to duty."

The naval officer C.A. Classens de Jongste dedicates very few words to Pompeii in the memoir of his stay in Naples, but he wants to provide the young with an example evoking military virtue (*Souvenirs d'une promenade au mont Vésuve*, 1841, pp. 30–32): "*Pompéïa*, la vestale chaste dont des mains profanes lèvent aujourd'hui avec mystère le voile sacré qui la couvre! Et sa voix murmure tout bas les choses cachées de la civilisation des temps de l'ancienne Rome. Écoutez, jeune soldat, écoutez, car les nobles faits, les actions sublimes doivent se proclamer! C'est aux portes de Pompéïa que les sentinelles romaines, les sentinelles de devoir ne désertèrent point le poste d'honneur. Ainsi, en observant religieusement leur consigne, elles donnèrent un grand exemple de cette discipline militaire dont les devoirs sont si rigoureux. Ainsi elles moururent avec gloire sous les coups enflammés d'un nouvel ennemi, mille fois plus redoutable que tous ceux contre lesquels elles luttèrent jamais!"

Overbeck becomes downright sentimental (1856, p. 27; 1865, p. 30): "Einen Soldaten, vielleicht die Schildwacht im Herculanerthor, fand man, den Speer in der Rechten, die Linke vor den Mund gehalten, in der ersten kleinen Grabnische vor dem Thore, welche man nach diesem Umstande trotz ihrer Inschrift zum Schilderhause gemacht hat. Auf die schräge gegenüberliegende überwölbte Halbkreisbank hatte sich, vielleicht um eine kurze Zeit von ihrer Flucht zu rasten, eine Mutter mit drei Kindern gesetzt, welche nicht mehr von dort aufstand."

The Frenchman Ernest Breton shows greater reserve in his informative and widely-read volume *Pompeia décrite et dessinée* (II ed. 1855, p. 98): "On a même écrit qu'un soldat, victime de la discipline, y avait été trouvé mort à son poste. Il en coûte de détruire cette glorieuse tradition." In the third edition (1870, p. 114) the sentry becomes a "martyr de la discipline", but the author notes that the document put together by Fiorelli now contradicts the hypothesis. Even the Englishman Thomas H. Dyer (*Pompeii. Its History, Buildings and Antiquities*, II ed. 1868, p. 579) is negative: "Unfortunately, however, this story is a pure fable. The Journals of the Excavations know nothing of this soldier, although they always particularly record the discovery of skeletons, because in most cases some coins or other property were found near them. Moreover, the place in question was no sentry-box, but a funeral monument of an Augustal named M. Cerrinius Restitutus, as appeared from an inscription."

John Murray in his *Handbook for Travellers in Southern Italy*, a kind of Baedeker and Italian Touring Club guidebook, says on the subject of the tomb of *Cerrinius Restitutus*: "The story of the skeleton of a soldier, fully armed, having been found here, led to its being considered at one time as a sentry-box; but as there is no authentic record of such a skeleton, the pleasing fable of the Roman soldier dying at his post must be abandoned (1763)" (VII ed. 1873, p. 230). Edited by August Mau, who was a great scholar of *res pompeiana*, the fourth edition of Overbeck's book – which is still indispensable reading matter for scholars – puts an end to the so-called sentry (1884, pp. 21, 400) with words similar to those of Dyer and Murray. It must in fact have been one of the guides' 'stories', and I do not know at what stage it first became part of the literature. Mariana Starke includes the sentry in her volume *Travels in Europe* (1828) and Twain probably read this book. Indeed, without epigraphical evidence, the niche being so near to the Herculaneum Gate does give the impression of a guard post, and thus has captured the imagination of many people.

The story, however, has never been completely forgotten as we find in some examples after 1860. The Lutheran pastor R. Schramm from Bremen writes in *Italienische Skizzen. Wanderungen durch Rom und Neapel* (I ed. 1881; II enlarged ed. 1890, pp. 265–266): "Bei einigen [of the skeletons] wird man von innigem Mitleiden ergriffen, auch wenn man sich vorhält, wie lange Jahrhunderte das alles schon vorüber und vergangen ist, bei andern kann man wenigstens die Theilnahme nicht versagen, einige muß man um ihrer Pflichttreue willen bewundern. So fand man am Herkulanerthor einen Soldaten, der dort als Schildwache aufgestellt den Posten nicht hat verlassen wollen. Noch hält die Rechte den Speer, die Linke hat er über den Mund gelegt, um sich gegen die erstickende Luft zu schützen, und gegen den Regen der glühenden Steine war er zum Schutze unter die vor dem Thor liegende kleine Grabnische getreten. In dieser Stellung hat ihn der Tod – jedenfalls durch Ersticken wie bei den meisten – ereilt. Schräg gegenüber an der Straße steht noch heute eine überwölbte halbkreisförmige Bank. Da rastete eine Mutter mit drei kleinen Kindern auf der Flucht, um nicht wieder aufzustehen."

The Italian novelist Emilio Garro chooses the soldier, whom he calls Romano, as the protagonist of *Pompeiana Juventus* written in 1942: the young man is simultaneously a good Roman and a good Christian who stays at his post until the very end (1942–XXII, pp. 226–228): "Alla Porta Ercolanese appunto il legionario Romano regolava l'afflusso dei fuggiaschi con altri due soldati. I tre archi della porta offrivano un riparo abbastanza sicuro, ma in quell'ultima furia vulcanica quello di mezzo crollò, seppellendo i due militi. Gli archi laterali, nel nembo di pietre e di cenere, furon presto ricolmi, e i profughi, che ancora lì intorno si aggiravano, o caddero per non più alzarsi, o ricacciati indietro, trovarono morte più lungi. Lì, presso un pilastro – diritto, immobile, appoggiato alla sua lunga asta – rimase il solo legionario Romano. Quello era il suo posto; di lì – egli pensava – non doveva muoversi … Quando, nella pioggia continua, se la sentì ammassata alla bocca, il legionario Romano volse in giro lo sguardo per vedere ancora lo spettacolo terribile che infuriava d'intorno, poi, – esempio sublime di fedeltà al dovere – chiuse gli occhi, abbandonandosi in Dio. E la cenere – che tutta ormai copriva Pompei – ricoperse anche lui."

Let us end this section with an interesting example. Oswald Spengler uses

the image of the sentry at the end of *Der Mensch und die Technik. Beitrag zu einer Philosophie des Lebens* (1932). Once again "Untergang des Abendlandes" has erupted where 'the coloureds', including the Russians, have seized industrial power from the 'whites'. The only conclusion is "Lieber ein kurzes Leben voll Taten und Ruhm als ein langes ohne Inhalt" (p. 88). Thus the final paragraph runs as follows (pp. 88–89): "Wir sind in diese Zeit geboren und müssen tapfer den Weg zu Ende gehen, der uns bestimmt ist. Es gibt keinen andern. Auf dem verlorenen Posten ausharren ohne Hoffnung, ohne Rettung, ist Pflicht. Ausharren wie jener römische Soldat, dessen Gebeine man vor einem Tor in Pompeji gefunden hat, der starb, weil man beim Ausbruch des Vesuv vergessen hatte, ihn abzulösen. Das ist Größe, das heißt Rasse haben. Dieses ehrliche Ende ist das einzige, das man dem Menschen nicht nehmen kann."[3]

Pompeii and the Bodies

Pompeii's archaeological realty invites one to make the dead city live again in imagination. One simple line of enquiry, but this time based on a real discovery, starts in the Villa of Diomedes, one of the most described monuments of Pompeii. Discovered in 1770 and partly left as it was at the time of the excavation, this affluent suburban house is a goal not to be missed, along with the tombs. For Goethe, the villa was "mehr Modell und Puppenschrank als Gebäude" (*Italienische Reise*, in *Hamburger Ausgabe*, München 1988, p. 198). Various skeletons were found – their number varies from eleven to twenty-two – and also the imprint of a female figure as we read in the report of December 12, 1763, published in the *Pompeianarum Antiquitatum Historia* (I, pp. 268–269): "Essendosi incominciato sin dalla passata settimana a levare della terra in un corridore, che resta ancora coperto con volta all'intorno del giardino dell'abitazione già detta, e ch'è quasi sotterraneo; ora essendosi scavato per non molti palmi il corridore suddetto, vi si sono trovati 18 scheletri di persone adulte, oltre quelli di un ragazzo e di un piccirillo. Si conosce bene che questi, e forse altri che si potranno ancora trovare continuandosi questo scavo, furono sorpresi in quel sito della casa, come il più lontano da soffrire qualunque insulto, ma che non poté riguardarli da una pioggia di cenere, che cadde dopo quella del lapillo, e che si conosce bene fu accompagnata con dell'acqua, la quale le aprì le strade per farla introdurre in tutte le parti, ove non aveva potuto introdursi la prima pioggia. Questa alluvione di materia fluidissima, resa dopo qualche tempo terra molto tenace, talmente abbracciò e circondò d'ogni intorno tutt'i corpi, che quelli hanno dovuto par [*sic*] la loro fragilità mancare. Questa materia ne ha conservato l'impronto ed il cavo; così si è conservato quello di una cassa di legno, e quello di una gran catasta di piccioli travicelli. Lo stesso è occorso degl'infelici che si sono scoperti, delle carni dei quali non ne sono restati che i vacui e gl'impronti nel terreno, e dentro questi le ossa niente smosse dal loro ordine; i capelli poi in parte si sono conservati attorno ad alcuni teschi, e si è traveduto alcune capigliature essere intrecciate. Degli abiti se ne sono trovate le ceneri, ma queste conservavano la qualità della materia, che ha attorniata la loro forma, sicché

N.L. Lemasle, Gioacchino Murat Visits the Villa of Diomedes, *first decade of the nineteenth century, pencil, ink and watercolour. Naples, Museo Nazionale di San Martino*

si distingue benissimo e le rarità delle loro trame, e della loro grossezza. Per dare una qualche testimonianza di quello che si asserisce avere osservato, ho pensato di far tagliare sino a 16 pezzi di quelli impronti di cadaveri, ove in uno fra gli altri si distingue il petto di una donna ricoperto da una veste, ed in tutti poi vi sono degli avanzi di vestimenti, fin di due e tre uno sopra dell'altro. Ho fatto anche prendere con diligenza un teschio, ove sono de' capelli, e tutte queste cose le ho mandate al Museo. Quel poco che ho potuto distinguere dei vestimenti, è stato, che molti avevano de' panni in testa, che gli scendevano fin sopra le spalle; che gli abiti si tenevano fino a due o tre uno sopra l'altro; che le calze erano di tela o panno tagliate come lunghi calzoni; che alcuni non avevano affatto scarpe. Riguardo però alle scarpe, può credersi che quelli osservati fossero de' bassi servi, distinguendosi bene e dagli ornamenti, e dalla sottigliezza delle vesti, e dalle monete che gli si sono trovate vicino, che una donna era distinta dalle altre." The director of the excavations, Francesco La Vega, digressed at length on these human remains, certainly by the standards of the usual descriptions of ongoing excavations. The report continues with a list of coins, jewelry and other objects found.

The oldest mention which I know of is in the travelling journal of François de Paule Latapie (1739–1823), who in 1776 read one of the first general accounts of Pompeii to the Académie Royale des Sciences, Lettres et Arts de Bordeaux ("Description des fouilles de Pompéi", *Rendiconti dell'Accademia di Napoli*, 28, 1953, pp. 223–248). There are always fewer human bones to be seen on the ground floor of the villa, because the tourists quite happily steal them, as Latapie did himself (p. 240): "Certaines personnes veulent en emporter des morceaux s'il leur est possible, ce que je n'ai pas manqué de faire, afin de posséder dans mon petit muséum un os qui ait plus de 17 siècles." More attention is paid to the dead by Jean-Claude Richard, Abbé de Saint-Non (*Voyage Pittoresque ou Description des Royaumes de Naples et de Sicile. Seconde Partie du Premier Volume, Contenant Une Description des Antiquités d'Herculanum, des Plans & des Détails de son Théâtre, avec une Notice abrégée des différents Spectacles des Anciens. Les Antiquités de Pompéi. La Description des Champs Phlégréens, & enfin celle de la Campanie & des Villes des Environs de Naples*, Paris 1782, p. 129): "C'est au bas de l'Escalier qui y [Cave K] conduit, que l'on a trouvé vingt-sept Squélettes de Femmes qui vraisemblablement, dans le trouble & l'effroi, s'étaient cachées dans cet endroit reculé. Elles s'étaient toutes refugiées, les unes auprès des autres, dans un des coins à côté de la Porte; & on a retrouvé avec leurs os, l'empreinte & la forme de leurs corps moulés & conservés dans les cendres, avec les détails de leurs habillemens. L'on fait voir même encore, au Muséum de Portici, l'empreinte de la gorge de l'une d'elles, avec leurs anneaux, leurs bracelets, les chaînes qu'elles portaient au col, & leurs boucles d'oreilles."

Charles-Marguerite Dupaty makes his Grand Tour in 1785 (*Lettres sur l'Italie par feu M. Dupaty*, 2 vols., Roma-Paris 1789) and feels moved by the tragedy in the Villa of Diomedes (II, pp. 131–132): "Je ne dois pas omettre un des monuments les plus curieux de ce cabinet célèbre; ce sont des fragments

d'enduit de cendres, qui lors d'une éruption du Vésuve, surprirent une femme, & l'enveloppèrent en entier. Ces cendres, pressées & durcies par le temps, autour de son corps, l'ont pris & moulé parfaitement. Plusieurs fragments de cet enduit conservent l'empreinte des formes particulieres qu'ils ont reçues. L'un possède la moitié du sein; il est d'une beauté parfaite; l'autre, une épaule; l'autre, une portion de la taille: ils nous révelent, de concert, que cette femme était jeune, qu'elle était grande, qu'elle était bien faite, & même qu'elle fuyait en chemise: car des morceaux de linge sont attachés à la cendre."
Hester Lynch Piozzi observes a year later in 1786 (*Observations and Reflections Made in the Course of a Journey through France, Italy, and Germany,* II, London 1789, pp. 35–36): "How dreadful are the thoughts which such a sight suggests! How very horrible the certainty, that such a scene might be all acted over again tomorrow; and that, who today are spectators, may become spectacles to travellers of a succeeding century, who mistaking our bones for those of the Neapolitans, may carry some of them to their native country back again perhaps; as it came into my head that a French gentleman was doing, when I saw him put a human bone into his pocket this morning, and told him I hoped he had got the jaw of a Gaulish officer, instead of a Roman soldier, for future reflections to energize upon."
The authoress is likewise impressed by the imprint of a foot and that of a "sick female, known to be so from the stole she wore, a drapery peculiar to her sex; her bed, converted into a substance like plaster of Paris, still retains the form and covering of her who perished quietly upon it, without ever making even an effort to escape" (p. 36).
René de Chateaubriand records his visit in 1804 in his *Voyage en Italie* (Paris 1824; *Œuvres romanesques et voyages*, II, Paris 1969, p. 1474), in which he sees the Villa of Diomedes "maison de campagne si connue ... C'est là que fut étouffée la jeune femme dont le sein s'est imprimée dans le morceau de terre que j'ai vu à Portici: la mort, comme un statuaire, a moulé sa victime."
Gell comments in his *Pompeiana* (III ed., p. 65): "It was Sir William Hamilton's opinion,[4] that this substance was deposited in a fluent state. The body in question was found some feet above the ancient level. She had probably struggled for some time against the continued showers of ashes, until sinking exhausted, she was covered with a slighter stratum, through which subsequent rains might have penetrated."
Let us also hear Breton on the subject (*Pompeia*: II ed., pp. 244–245; III ed., pp. 299–301): "Au moment de l'éruption, 17 femmes et enfants crurent trouver un refuge assuré sous ces voûtes impénétrables; des provisions qu'ils y avaient portées leur assuraient l'existence pour quelques jours; mais bientôt les cendres fines et brûlantes y pénétrèrent par les soupiraux, une vapeur ardente remplit la galerie; les malheureux se précipitèrent vers la porte ... il était trop tard! Tous périrent étouffés et à moitié ensevelis. C'est là qu'on les a retrouvés au bout de 17 siècles, la tête encore enveloppée des vêtements dont ils s'étaient voilé le visage, soit pour se préserver des cendres ardentes, soit par un acte suprême de décence et de résignation." Our sight is arrested by "les empreintes des seins,

des bras et des épaules d'une jeune fille d'une amirable beauté." Judging from her expensive clothing, she is perhaps the daughter of the owner. The father leaves his family, but finds death a little further on; he has the doorkey with him (p. 246). Dyer too changes his tone (pp. 493–494): "This [the final turn of events] the reader will probably be inclined to think might do very well for the conclusion of a romance, but why invent such sentimental stories to figure in a grave historical account? It is a remarkable instance, perhaps the strongest which has yet occurred, of the peculiar interest which the discoveries at Pompeii possess, as introducing us to the homes, nay, to the very persons of a long-forgotten age, that every circumstance of this tale can be verified by evidence little less than conclusive."

In Gautier's tale *Arria Marcella* (1852), mentioned above, the young Octavien becomes infatuated with the imprint of a woman's breast found in the Villa of Diomedes (C. Aziza, *Pompéi. Le rêve sous les ruines*, Paris 1992, pp. 501–527). He goes on thinking that he has met the girl, whom he calls Arria Marcella because of a presumed link with Arrius Diomedes, and follows her. The story lurches between the current day and 23rd–24th August 79 A.D. and the lovers abandon themselves to an embrace in the Villa of Diomedes. Her father, who has just converted to Christianity, then enters and tries to warn his daughter off such a liason (pp. 524–525): "Arria, Arria, dit le personnage austère d'un ton de reproche, le temps de ta vie n'a-t-il pas suffi à tes déportements, et faut-il que tes infâmes amours empiètent sur les siècles qui ne t'appartiennent pas? Ne peux-tu laisser les vivants dans leur sphère, ta cendre n'est donc pas encore refroidie depuis le jour où tu mourus sans repentir sous la pluie de feu du volcan? Deux mille ans de mort ne t'ont donc pas calmée, et tes bras voraces attirent sur ta poitrine de marbre, vide de cœur, les pauvres insensés enivrés par tes philtres.

– Arrius, grâce, mon père, ne m'accablez pas au nom de cette réligion morose qui ne fut jamais la mienne; moi, je crois à nos anciens dieux qui aimaient la vie, la jeunesse, la beauté, le plaisir; ne me replongez pas dans le pâle néant. Laissez-moi jouir de cette existence que l'amour m'a rendue."

Thus Gautier turns the world upside down: the father comes to life again and finds out what will happen to him and to his daughter. The girl – the only one not to lose her head – gives herself spontaneously to the modern boy, and he, Octavien, feels no scruples at having a relationship with a 'pagan' woman. On the contrary, he experiences "des élans insensés vers un idéal retrospectif" and compares himself to Faust (p. 512).

Here is Giuseppe Fiorelli's comment, taken from a lecture on *Pompei nella letteratura* (Napoli 1888, pp. 29–30): "Questo cachet de beauté, trovato nella casa di Diomede, porge al Gautier il destro di evocare nella sua fantasia la fanciulla pallida e bruna, dalle linee fidiache, della quale una nobile forma, caduta in polvere da duemila anni, grazie al capriccio della eruzione, è pervenuta sino a noi."

Unfortunately, as Amedeo Maiuri had to establish,[5] the imprint of the breast no longer exists.

Pompeii and Politics

Pompeii and Herculaneum have also become a political issue, as we see from the passage of Spengler quoted above. Maiuri excavated with the support of the current Fascist regime. His first popular pamphlet on the subject (*Ercolano*, "Visioni italiche" series, Roma-Novara-Paris 1932) begins with a quote from the Duce of 24th October 1931: "Potete offrire al mondo panorami incantevoli e città dissepolte che non hanno uguali sulla faccia della terra." Mussolini spells out the unique nature of the cities of Vesuvius, in a way that the Bourbon king Charles might well have done. Let us examine three examples from literature. The tragic state of Poland around 1830 provokes a bitter lament from the Polish author J. Ursen Niemcewicz, who had visited Pompeii in 1784 (in T. Mikocki, *À la recherche de l'art antique. Les voyageurs polonais en Italie dans les années 1750–1830,* Wroclaw 1988, p. 100): "Il me semblait y vivre, y reconnaître la maison en laquelle j'ai vécu. Selon moi, c'est un des plus intéressants monuments de l'Antiquité. Ciel! Pourquoi n'ai-je pas vécu à Pompéi, n'y ai-je pas été enseveli, pour ne pas voir l'actuelle perte de ma patrie."

Leopardi compares Topaia, the mouse-world in his *Paralipomeni della Batracomiomachia,* to a subterranean Herculaneum and laments the state of neglect in which Naples finds itself (he is alluding to the revolution of 1820). His criticisms are directed at the Accademia Ercolanese – of which Francesco Maria Avellino had been the tenured secretary since 1832 – with regard to the papyri, but also at the attitude of the Parthenopean intellectuals who did not receive Leopardi's ideas favourably.[6] The poet begins with a description of the mice's living quarters; they have palaces, statues, columns as in every big city, but they do not need light (III, 2, 6–10). They live hidden away, like the treasures of Herculaneum (III, 2, 11–14):

"11

D'Ercolano così sotto Resina, / Che d'ignobili case e di taverne / Copre la nobilissima ruina, / Al tremolar di pallide lucerne / Scende a veder la gente pellegrina / Le membra afflitte e pur di fama eterne, / Magioni e scene e templi e colonnati / Allo splendor del giorno ancor negati.

12

Certo se un suol germanico o britanno / Queste ruine nostre ricoprisse, / Di faci a visitar l'antico danno / Più non bisogneria ch'uom si servisse, / E d'ogni spesa in onta e d'ogni affanno / Pompei, ch'ad ugual sorte il fato addisse, / All'aspetto del Sol tornata ancora / Tutta, e non pur sì poca parte fora.

13

Vergogna sempiterna e vitupero, / D'Italia non dirò, ma di chi prezza / Disonesto tesor più che il mistero / Dell'aurea antichità porre in chiarezza, / E riscossa di terra allo straniero / Mostrare ancor l'italica grandezza. / Lor sia data dal ciel giusta mercede, / Se pur ciò non indarno al ciel si chiede.

14

E mercè s'abbia non di riso e d'ira, / Di ch'ebbe sempre assai, ma d'altri danni / L'ipocrita canaglia, onde sospira / L'Europa tutta invan tanti e tanti anni /

I papiri ove cauta ella delira, / Scacciando ognun, su i mercenari scanni; / Razza a cagion di cui mi dorrebb'anco / Se boia e forche ci venisser manco."

Candido Augusto Vecchi (1810–1869), a supporter of Garibaldi, writes, around 1860, a kind of "scènes de vie de Pompéi" in the manner of Balzac (*Pompei*, Torino 1864) dedicated to those who had made their mark on history, and like the author had struggled for the unity of Italy. He may well have been a great patriot, but he is not much of a writer. He sees in Pompeii the symbol of what the new Italy should be like. He uses the interest sparked off by pagan religions as opposition to the Catholic church. Here are a few gems of his prose.
A certain Marcus Holconius Rufus, a retired general and politician, is not asked if he has slept well (p. 56), but instead: "Fugli propizio Morfeo?"
He and his friends observe some unsavoury customs in Pompeii which to Vecchi's eyes can be compared to the modern world (p. 61): "Sono passati diciotto secoli e la tradizione rimane ancor verde. Vi ha tal gente in Napoli che lautamente vive di una siffatta speculazione ladra ed infame. Il cattolicesimo vi presta la sua mano sacrilega. – Sozzi frati colla bisaccia sul collo. – Sozzi preti con un bussolo che scuotono nelle botteghe nel nome santo di Dio. – Sozza bordaglia, coperta di un sacco, cinto da una corda sui lombi, chiede danaro e l'ottiene a pro di turpi speculatori e per cause non vere. – E quel buon popolo – il migliore d'Italia per pronta intelligenza, per docilità di carattere, per esuberanza di cuore – su ricchissimo suolo, vegeta sudicio, lacero ed infingardo. – Demoralizzato dai preti, commette opere inique e crudeli. Abbuiato dalla paura, dimentica il domani della vita e sciupa il sopravanzo dei suoi guadagni nello inutile tentativo di spegnere il sacro incendio del purgatorio cattolico, apostolico, romano."
In another excerpt he pontificates as follows: "I sacerdoti antichi dicevano – 'Spendete; e le Ombre amate godranno nei Campi-Elisi delle ricchezze che avrete profuso nel loro mortaio!' –. E i sacerdoti moderni pur dicono – 'Spendete; e allor suoneremo campane, canteremo, borbotteremo in latino e tratteremo con Dio come fosse un giudice borbonico; e a furia di danari dati noi, noi costringeremo lui a riconoscere in un'anima ribalda una onesta' –."

Pompeii, City of Sin

We have already seen how freely Gautier can use Pompeii as the setting for a love affair. For many authors there are rather too many pointers to sin in the pictures of nudes, phalluses (of which there used to be a whole showcase in the Museum at Portici) and graffiti (which are quoted less often than election inscriptions).
Jérôme De Lalande (1732–1807) in his *Voyage en Italie* (VII, Paris 1786, p. 435) is forced to make a general reflection when he sees a collection of phalluses in the Museum at Portici: "Au reste, les villes de la Campanie, Capoue & Baies, étaient regardées plus que autres endroits de l'Italie, comme des lieux de volupté & de license. Vénus était spéciellement honorée à Herculanum, & l'on trouve des attributs de ce culte obscène sur beaucoup de lampes de bronze,

où l'imagination s'est épuisée dans les formes les plus bizarres & les plus libidineuses; mais on ne les a point exposées dans le cabinet de Portici."
Is this hypocrisy or sincerity? Stanislas-Marie-César Famin publishes an important volume on the 'Gabinetto Segreto' in Naples: *Musée Royal de Naples. Peintures, bronzes et statues érotiques du Cabinet Secret avec notes explicatives de plusieurs auteurs* (Paris 1832; I consulted the Bruxelles-Paris edition of 1876), in which the first image is of copulation on the wedding night, the second is of "un débauche" involving two lovers and the third is a brothel scene. In the preface he describes dreadful things of bygone times, including the biblical, mentioning examples of cruelty in the Old Testament (p. II). Nowadays, according to Famin, we live in a calmer and more serene age: "Nous n'ignorons pas que quelques aveugles partisans des temps anciens prétendent que les nudités obscènes qui apparaissent continuellement dans la littérature comme dans les représentations artistiques des beaux temps de la Grèce et de Rome ne sont que les indices de la simplicité et de la candeur. Les sauvages mêmes de nos jours peuvent, disent-ils, servir de nouvel appui à cette hypothèse. Qu'est-ce à dire? La pudeur n'est donc qu'hypocrisie; les anciens dont le langage et les habitudes étaient empreints de tant d'obscénités valaient donc mieux que nous qui jetons le voile épais du mystère sur nos plus innocentes faiblesses?"
Once again, is this hypocrisy or is he really sincere? Defensive words are also to be found in the preface to the eighth volume of Louis Barré's *Herculaneum et Pompéi* (1877) which also deals with the same collection of pornographic material in the National Museum. There is now a fine new edition of this, with extensive commentary by Laurentino García y García and Luciana Jacobelli (2001). Barré underlines the importance of erotic images and objects in helping us better understand classical authors such as Aristophanes (pp. 2–3): "Le moraliste, le plus zélé, pour peu qu'il fût poëte en même temps, si on lui donnait le pouvoir d'anéantir, par un seul effort de sa pensée, les productions licencieuses que nous ont leguées les anciens, oserait-il prononcer l'infaillible anathème, et mutiler Aristophane, Anacréon, Théocrite, Horace, Plaute, Ovide, Tibulle, Catulle, Juvénal, Martial et Pétrone. Eh bien! j'ose le dire, ce ne serait pas un moindre sacrilège que de souhaiter l'anéantissement des collections pornographiques ou d'en blâmer la publication, puisque ces collections complètent et expliquent tous ces écrivains." Then, in a further attempt to justify the publication of this book, he tries to show that the objects are not actually *obscene* (pp. 6–7): "D'ailleurs, la plupart des monuments dont il s'agit sont vraiment chastes dans leur obscénité même, chastes par la sainteté des idées qu'ils devaient réveiller. Il faut soigneusement distinguer, parmi ces monuments, une partie hiératique ou religieuse, une partie purement licencieuse. Ces deux classes correspondent à deux états différents de l'esprit humain." It is worth noting that Famin's illustrations are frequently more explicit, or rather less censored, than those in Barré's work.
While on the subject, I would maintain that it is quite likely that in many of the luxurious volumes of the nineteenth century (Zahn, Ternite etc) which

contain mythological scenes, the choice of naked gods and heroes is not random but has a mild pornographic undercurrent.

Pompeii does not feature widely in the literature as a city of sin, but there are, particularly in France, works which underline how pleasant life must have been in Pompeii, thanks to the mildness of the climate and the richness of the terrain. Even if the eruption of Vesuvius put an end to it all, Maxime Formont puts the emphasis on the love between Elius and Psyché in *Visions antiques. La Danseuse. Roman* (Paris 1914). Here, the reader finds *topoi* such as opulent dinners, luxurious furniture in highly affluent houses and villas, people who do nothing all day but take baths and go on trips, make love, eat and drink. Nice places like Baia, Capri, Posillipo and other *loci amoeni* on the Bay of Naples serve to make life even pleasanter. The lovers take a trip to Herculaneum (p. 258): "La riche Herculanum ne les garda pas longtemps, malgré la beauté de ses maisons, de ses théâtres et de ses temples: il y régnait un faste importun pour des amoureux; la présence d'un grand nombre de familles illustres y maintenait, au milieu des douces campagnes d'Italie, la même étiquette qu'à Rome et le même train d'existence. Aussi lui préférèrent-ils Pompeia, célèbre par ses vins, ses délices et ses roses."

Even more recently Norbert Rouland has evoked the *topos* of Pompeii as a happy place in his novel set in the first century B.C. revolution period entitled *Les Lauriers de cendre* (Paris 1984). The couple Lucius and Aurelia are enjoying themselves here before he is recalled to Rome to resume his duties as magistrate. For Lucius, Pompeii is a bacchic city (p. 232): "Je suis allé en ville hier, et Jupiter n'y est guère présent. Tandis que Bacchus … Partout on voit ses statues, à l'angle des rues, dans les jardins … Et son temple, près de l'amphithéâtre! Il est plus richement décoré que celui du Père des dieux." He shows Aurelia the city, and together they decide that Pompeii is a mixture of elements which are Greek, Roman and local (p. 237): "Aurelia s'exclama: – Quel mélange! Des dieux grecs, romains, italiques … Il ne manque plus que ton Samhain celte!

Lucius répondit en riant: – Les Pompéiens sont hospitaliers. Ils ont de bonnes raisons – reprit-il en passant son bras autour de la taille d'Aurelia.

Elle déposa sur sa joue un rapide baiser, et lui demanda en souriant: – Ils aiment donc autant les Grecs que ta mère?

– Mais Pompéi est grecque! Tous ses habitants te diront que c'est Héraklès qui a fondé leur ville … A Pompéi on trouve de tout: des grecs, des Samnites, des juifs, des orientaux …

Et des Romains! – ajouta Aurelia en riant."

Epilogue

As is evident from these excerpts, I have used a potpourri of three kinds of texts: literary works (poetry and prose), travellers' journals, and other syntheses, though up to the end of the last century, one might say that there is not much difference between them. Even archaeologists try to use a style which is attractive to the layman. With Nissen, Mau and Fiorelli, archaeology activity in Pompeii became professional, a full-time job for people who did nothing but archaeology. This is not to say that their writings, or those of their successors, are unreadable: one has only to think of the beautiful pages of Maiuri in *Pompei ed Ercolano. Tra case ed abitanti.* People write well or badly, but the important point is the difference we find between fine prose and scientfic texts dealing with the buried cities. At a certain point, the layman is no longer capable of following scientific developments and has to rely on guidebooks of a general nature which become progressively out of date as new things are discovered. I refer, for example, to the *Pompeianarum Antiquitatum Historia.* After 1860, all the guidebooks and handbooks clearly show that the authors have compared their texts with those of the old sources: Overbeck, Dyer and Breton.

The rather over-simplified guidebooks written by the superintendents and excavation directors which were published after Fiorelli's in 1875, as detailed as it is dry, mark a step backwards; no longer do they paint colourful and detailed images to be dipped into at will. For poets and novelists, in search of sparks of inspiration, the absence of guidebooks can nevertheless be substituted by the literature of the nineteenth century. Anyone wanting to gather information these days, as Marguerite Yourcenar did, would not find it an easy task. But even without a guidebook, anyone can create his/her own picture of Pompeii, a city which died in 79 A.D. but came alive again, from 1748 onwards, not kissed by a prince, but excavated by a king.

[1] This essay is an extended version of *Una città mummificata: qualche aspetto della fortuna di Pompei nella letteratura europea ed americana*, in P.G. Guzzo (ed.), *Pompei scienza e società. 250° Anniversario degli Scavi di Pompei. Convegno internazionale, Napoli 25-27 novembre 1998*, Milano 2001, pp. 9–18. See also: C. Aziza, *Pompéi. Le rêve sous les ruines*, Paris 1992; C. Dahl, "Recreations of Pompeii", *Archaeology*, 9, 1956, pp. 182–191; F. Fernández Murga, "Pompeya en la literatura española", in *Annali dell'Istituto Universitario Orientale di Napoli. Sezione romana,* 7.1, Napoli 1965; W. Leppmann, *Pompeji. Eine Stadt in Literatur und Leben*, München 1966 (*Pompeii in Fact and Fiction*, London 1968); T. Mikocki, *A la recherche de l'art antique. Les voyageurs polonais en Italie dans les années 1750–1830*, Wroclaw 1988; M. Reinhold, *Classica Americana. The Greek and Roman Heritage in the United States*, Detroit 1986, pp. 265–279; J. Seznec, "Herculaneum and Pompeii in French Literature of the Eighteenth Century", *Archaeology*, 2, 1948, pp. 150–158; V. Kockel, *Pompeji, Der Neue Pauly. Rezeptions- und Wissenschaftsgeschichte 15/2*, Stuttgart 2002, pp. 472–490; T. Fitzon, "Pompeji/Rezeption des freigelegten Pompeji in Literatur und Film", in *ibidem*, pp. 490–495. A major reference for bibliographical research is L. García y García, *Nova Bibliotheca Pompeiana. 250 anni di bibliografia archeologica*, Roma 1998, an inexhaustible source for the Vesuvian cities.

[2] V. Kockel, *Die Grabbauten vor dem Herkulaner Tor in Pompeji*, Mainz 1983, pp. 47–51: "Süd 1, Grab des M. Cerrinius Restitutus". On p. 49 is the history of the excavation referring to the correct interpretation of C. Bonucci, *Pompéi décrite, ou précis historique des excavations depuis l'année 1748 jusqu'à nos jours. Traduction de la Troisième édition italienne par C.J.,* Napoli 1828, p. 74.

[3] My thanks to Gemma Jansen and Robert Kragting for this very valuable reference.

[4] The explanation is indeed found in W. Hamilton, "Account of the Discoveries at Pompeii", *Archaeologia: or Miscellaneous Tracts Relating to Antiquity*, 4, 1777, pp. 160–175, above all pp. 172–173.

[5] A. Maiuri, *Pompei ed Ercolano. Tra case ed abitanti*, Napoli 1958 (1998 ed., pp. 39–42).

[6] Leopardi's writings are quoted by R. Damiani, M.A. Rigon (eds.), *G. Leopardi. Poesie e Prose*, I, Milano 1987. See also the informative article by V. Bracco, "Leopardi e le antichità napoletane", in *Leopardi e il mondo antico. Atti del V Convegno Internazionale di studi leopardiani (Recanati 1980)*, Firenze 1982, pp. 301–319. The latter also notes that Michele Ruggiero, the future director of the excavations, designed Leopardi's tomb at San Vitale (p. 303).

Fabrizio Pesando Shadows of Light: Cinema, *Peplum* and Pompeii

The Earliest Beginnings

On the wave of emotion created by the first public projection of a moving picture, one perceived that with this discovery "spectacle, the newspaper and the school of tomorrow" were born, but people could hardly have imagined the extent to which this prophecy would come true in the world of the future. The thousands of images which are now part of today's daily reality are only the descendents of those fleeting shadows of light which were shown for the first time in Paris on 28th December 1895. And among the filtered and distorted images that have assailed us in more than a century of cinematic production, a goodly part has been dedicated to an era as distant from us as the outer space depicted in the films of Stanley Kubrick and Ridley Scott; a world and an era that the collective imagination perceives confusedly and which goes under the composite name of 'Greco-Roman civilisation'. The inexhaustible source of all these possible reconstructions, be they correct or distorted, is of course Pompeii, the most intact archaeological site ever excavated in the Western Mediterranean, where life suddenly stopped one day in August 79 A.D. It was as if it were fixed for ever on a huge photographic plate, ready to be looked at by the inquiring eyes of scholars, the excited gaze of cultivated travellers or the surprised gapings of casual visitors. Thus, it is no surprise that the cinema has made good use, more or less accurately, of this hoard of images, sometimes with stories actually set in one of the towns which was buried by the rage of Vesuvius, and sometimes – and this is perhaps the more interesting aspect – with casual and more or less involuntary references, which goes to show how profoundly Pompeii and Herculaneum and the objects found there can, all by themselves, evoke the scenario of the ancient world.

Thus it is not by chance that among the historical films with a Greco-Roman setting produced in the early days of film-making was one based on one of the most famous historical novels of the nineteenth century: Edward George Bulwer-Lytton's *Last Days of Pompeii*. Through its images, a first attempt was made to tell the dark story of love, death and destruction which interweaves the destinies of the refined Glaucus, the treacherous priest of Isis, Arbaces, the devoted slave-girl Nidia and the rich young Pompeian women Julia and Ione with the moment when Vesuvius erupts. Film repertoires report the author, the date and the length of this film: Walter Booth, 1900, 80 feet. These few moments of footage were only the first of many film versions of this English novel, and it is worth saying a few words about its fidelity to the narrative and to the places described.

But before surveying the history of this particular kind of historic film, we must take a step backwards, because the first interaction between a paying audience and a Pompeian-inspired setting goes back much further in time to the history of opera. Mozart's *Magic Flute* was first produced on 30th September 1791 in the Theater auf der Weiden in Vienna and was directed by Emanuel Schikaneder. The playbill printed for the occasion recorded that the libretto was also written by Schikaneder and that messers Gayl and Nessthaler were

Gayl's and Nessthaler's sets for Mozart's Magic Flute *(Act I, scene I and Act II, scene XXV), Vienna, 1791*

responsible for the sets. The opening scene of the first performance showed Tamino in a somewhat desolate and rocky place,in the centre of which was a round temple, whose entrance consisted of a *pronaos* of five columns, flanked by two projecting parts with niches. In a study on the cult of Isis, it was pointed out with perhaps understandable amazement, how strange it was that this temple, of which Sarastro is the High Priest of the Sun and the Chief Priest of Isis, had so few Isiac details on the original set design, and was so bereft of all that grand magnificence which we associate with the Egypt of the pharaohs. The reason for this apparent incongruousness is quite simple: the small temple is indeed a temple of Isis, but its design is inspired not by Egyptian ruins or remains, which only begin to be known in the West after Napoleon's expedition, but by the only example of this type of sanctuary known at the time the opera was first produced, namely the Temple of Isis at Pompeii. Its position, between barren walls of rock, and the shape of the temple itself were merely a reconstruction – from memory – of the Pompeian temple, which although completely unearthed, was still surrounded by heaps of lapilli between 1764 and 1766. The same applies to the hall of the initiates, reached through an arched doorway, which appears in the second act and which made almost spoken reference to the *ekklesiasterion* faced onto the west colonnade of the sanctuary. But we must not be surprised by the explicit reference to the small temple at Pompeii. Either because of its exceptional state of preservation, or because of the cult itself which inspired the masonic principles that were currently fashionable in many European courts, the temple became the goal of pilgrimages in those days: some of those early visitors carved their names on the stucco of the cella or of the *purgatorium*, among them Joseph II of Austria, a great power in European freemasonry, and Mozart himself who managed to see the ruins of Pompeii during his second trip to Italy.

Thirty years later, on November 19th 1825 at the San Carlo Theatre in Naples, the first night of Giovanni Pacini's *L'ultimo giorno di Pompei* (The Last Day of Pompeii) was staged, with a libretto by the poet Leone Tottola. The plot of the opera – which has no links whatsoever with Bulwer-Lytton's novel published nine years later – centres on an attempt by the tribune Appius to seduce Octavia, wife of Sallustius who was elected town magistrate in that fated year of 79 A.D. Rejected by her, Appius then goes on to accuse Octavia unjustly of immoral conduct with a young man during a party (his name is Clodius, which brings to mind the famous Roman tribune who profaned the mysteries of the Bona Dea in Caesar's own house). Octavia is condemned by her own husband to be buried alive, something which we know was done in Rome to Vestal Virgins who broke their vow of chastity, but the sudden re-awakening of Vesuvius drives one of the slanderers to repent, so that Sallustius reunites with Octavia and they both try to flee the city.

The audience was regaled not only with a plot which unravelled under the menacing threat of the eruption but also with a reconstruction of the splendid ceremony of Sallustius' election, against the solemn setting of the Forum.

There were other late nineteenth-century operas inspired more or less freely by *The Last Days of Pompeii*, but which have not stood the test of time, due to the poor quality of their music, and which now only form part of a long list of compositions that take Vesuvius as their backdrop.

The Last Days of Pompeii

There are two main Greco-Roman subjects which dominate this new art form of cinema at the beginning of the twentieth century, with multiple versions, sometimes only a few years apart, as if to mark the rapid progress made in cinematographic technique. One of them is *Quo Vadis?*, the story of the first great persecution of the Christians under Nero (there are four versions: 1901; two appearing almost simultaneously in 1912; and 1924) and of course *The Last Days of Pompeii* (this too in four versions: 1900; two in 1913; 1926). These two apparently contrasting themes have something in common, namely the possibility of reconstructing complex scenes using more and more stunning special effects. The first film versions of these stories in fact spend little time on the story of Marcus Vinicius, Lycia, Ursus and the first Christians, or on that of Glaucus, Ione and Nidia, but concentrate above all on two key action moments in the plot, namely the fire of Rome in 64 A.D. and the eruption of Vesuvius in 79 A.D.

The success of these historically-inspired films which so dominated both the early and later days of cinema, resided in the possibility of exploiting the new medium to the full, and providing the viewer simultaneously with a glimpse of a distant world and the sight of the violent destructive forces of nature. In Giovanni Pastrone's famous *Cabiria,* (1914) which could amaze and inspire directors of the calibre of David Wark Griffith with its powerful plot (behind which, as we know, there was more Salgari than D'Annunzio), there are unforgettable scenes, such as Hannibal crossing the Alps, the ritual fire lit for Moloch and the terrifying eruption of Etna, and in one of the last *peplum* movies to be produced in Italy (*79 A.D.*, by G. Parolini, 1962) the climax of this highly predictable plot centres yet again on the eruption of Vesuvius. But in this case also, film-making was improving on something which had been seen before. Mario Verdone has very convincingly identified the common source of so many Greco-Roman settings in early film as not only the world of theatre and opera but also, and perhaps above all, that of late nineteenth-century circus, in which – as in the case of the famous Barnum Circus – shows such as *Nero, or the Destruction of Rome* were put on, described by contemporary playbills as "the most amazing and regal historical production of any age".

The early cinematographic productions of *The Last Days of Pompeii* also reach this level of sensationalism; the images of Eleuterio Rodolfi's 1913 version, produced for Ambrosio of Turin, are still very impressive in their use of special effects for the eruption of Vesuvius, the destruction of the city and the flight of the citizens driven away by the volcanic explosions. And against this often ill-defined background, real Pompeian buildings appear; here and there among scenes of ruin and devastation, it is possible to recognise some public

monuments, above all the *Capitolium*, whose falling columns crush dozens of fleeing people.
The backdrop of the narrative scenes is more conventional; a herm indicates that we are in a refined garden, interiors are marked by trappings and furniture, while in the parts dealing with Arbaces' unbridled and immoral lifestyle we are presented with decadence, spelled out by weighty tapestries, Egyptian symbols and heavy puffs of incense.
The most accurate reproduction of the ancient world, in terms of reference to the sources, is certainly that of Amleto Palermi's and Carmine Gallone's famous silent movie, produced by Grandifilms in 1926. For an archaeologist, or anyone who knows Pompeii, it is a real pleasure to be able to recognise public and private buildings in which, in many cases, paintings and decorations now lost have been reproduced with absolute fidelity. Beneath this highly accurate representation are hidden seams of contemporary Pompeian studies. This film presents the first panoramic view of the ruins of Pompeii, a valuable glimpse of the state of excavations during the first quarter of the twentieth century as well as close-ups of the excavated monuments where the scenes were shot. These, combined with the rather jumpy footage that joins them with the studio shots, makes one appreciate the achievements of the great Pompeian photographers of the second half of the nineteenth century – such as Giorgio Sommer, Giacomo Brogi, Michele Amodio – who were capable of producing the most sophisticated reproductions of the city's main public and private buildings and of publishing the first versions of that highly successful series of photographs known as *Pompei, Com'era, com'è* (Pompeii, How It Was, How It Is). And behind the precise reproductions of the paintings which we see in the houses of Glaucus, Ione or in the Stabian Baths, there is also the vast amount of work which must have gone into making the huge cork model of Pompeii, started in 1821 by Domenico Padiglione and updated continually until 1939. The effort which went into making the Pompeian backdrops to the scenes is particularly notable in the view of the garden in Julia's house, where the *nymphaeum* of the House of the Large Fountain is reproduced – very suitable for a film with its tragic masks – in the interior of Glaucus' house (the House of the Tragic Poet, with a few too many theatrical masks), and also in the reconstruction of the Temple of Isis. Behind it you can make out not only the *summa cavea* of the Large Theatre, but also the top of the cistern between the theatre and the adjoining Samnite Palaestra. Also most accurate are the spaces of the Forum, the Amphitheatre, on which the now-lost paintings of the external balustrade are shown, and the Stabian Baths. Indeed it was the reproduction of this building, with its huge Palaestra seething with athletes, that proved most demanding. In reality, the long scene shot in the baths – which had been excavated about twenty years before the book was published – does not feature in the original plot and can thus be seen as a deliberate innovation on the part of the screenwriters. The reconstruction of the swimming pool and the two projecting buildings which flank it on its shorter sides recreates

Palermi-Gallone's Last Days of Pompeii *(1926): Glaucus' house*

a space which is not usually obvious to the visitor's eye and allows us to appreciate the rich decoration of the stuccoed surfaces which has now more or less disappeared. The positioning of sculptural athletic groups inside the Palaestra (the Borghese Warrior, the Discobolus, the Wrestlers) may be arbitrary but it is also quite probable. The whole scene, the most complex in terms of the extras employed, becomes one of the most successful of the entire film, even if the camera does manage to penetrate into the most secret recesses of the building (a wonder only possible in cinema!) namely into the women's baths where semi-naked girls wash themselves and chat. In these nude scenes, uncensored in the Italian version, one can note an aesthetic gratification that spurred the film-makers to measure themselves against the nineteenth-century illustrations and paintings on the same subject, such as Domenico Morelli's *Pompeian Bath* (1861), in which the static painted figures contrast with the impact of the moving images.

At any rate, beyond the commercial success, which was the more surprising considering the profound crisis surrounding the Italian film industry at the time, Palermi-Gallone's *Gli ultimi giorni di Pompeii* shows its limitations in the plot of its narrative, as if all the energies of its producer and director had been concentrated and used up on the minor scenes. Only the description of Arbaces' lustful and impious lifestyle redeems the narrative, and significantly, because it is not dependent on strict adherence to historical sources. The house of this treacherous priest of Isis is a complete invention, full of mysterious objects, with clear geometric spaces and decorative elements which owe not a little to expressionism.

But if this final colossal of the Italian silent cinema has its defects, the subsequent film versions of Bulwer-Lytton's novel are notable for their decline, partly attributed to a dearth of inspiration.

Two films in this series – a genre which was to be abandoned for a long period because of the excessive costs – are Paolo Moffa's *Last Days of Pompeii* (1948) and that of Mario Bonnard, made with the collaboration of Sergio Leone in 1959, both of them superficial in terms of narrative and accuracy of setting. In the Franco-Italian version, the conventions of historical films are quite obvious; Pompeii has become a cardboard cut-out city which can be easily assembled for scenes set in Rome as well as any part of the imaginary ancient world. Bonnard's film, perhaps as a result of his collaboration with Sergio Leone, becomes a parody of the *peplum* genre, if anything because of the producer's choice of the muscle-bound actor Steve Reeves who had become famous briefly for his interpretation of Hercules in various *peplum* movies. The choice of this actor transformed the sensitive and refined Glaucus into an unsophisticated and boorish centurion.

Here and there, Augusto Leda's set shows us various Pompeian buildings (the Villa of the Mysteries, the Forum) but most efforts seem to have gone, with only partial success, into livening up the inside of a *thermopolium* to create an atmosphere that predates the saloons of future 'spaghetti westerns'.

Palermi-Gallone's Last Days of Pompeii *(1926): scenes from the Stabian Baths*

Pompeian Scenarios

In the great age of epic films, dominated by the million-dollar productions of *Quo Vadis?* (M. LeRoy, 1951), *The Robe* (H. Koster, 1953), *Ben Hur* (W. Wyler, 1959) right up to the financially disastrous *Cleopatra* (J.L. Mankiewicz, 1963) – which as a matter of fact put an end to this kind of film and made redundant the vast film sets of Cinecittà used by the big American companies – Pompeii with its buildings, wall-paintings and trappings, became a sort of inexhaustible mine for period scenery and settings. Even in a classic film like *Spartacus* (S. Kubrick, 1960), which is rich in suggestive imagery, we find fragments of the Vesuvian city, taken out of their own context, used only to evoke an authentic Roman flavour. In the scene where the Senator Gracchus and Varinia, Spartacus' slave wife meet, the opulence and elegance of the house of this old defender of the Republic (Charles Laughton, once again playing a magisterial role) are rapidly but unmistakably etched on our consciousness by images of the large decoration of the Villa of the Mysteries on one of the walls of the room. This kind of reference had been made in earlier films, and will also be found in a genre vastly different from the *peplum* movie, namely in the satires of Monty Python. In the first postwar Italian colossal, *Fabiola* (A. Blasetti, 1947), which is set in fourth-century Rome, near late-antique buildings such as the Basilica of Maxentius (rashly identified as one of the buildings used by the *praefectus urbi* long before Filippo Coarelli's accurate and detailed study established it as such) there appear buildings of obvious Vesuvian inspiration, like Fabiola's own house, modelled on a typical Pompeian country villa. And in *Monty Python's Life of Brian* (T. Jones, 1979) one of the eccentric and vainglorious Jewish conspirators emerges – as if out of a manhole – from the centre of the mosaic of the House of the Faun, which features an embracing satyr and nymph, a symbol of Roman lust shown on the bath building in an improbably Romanized Jerusalem. In Luigi Magni's *Scipio the African* (1970) his grotesque characters move about in a Pompeii whose buildings are in the state in which Vesuvius and sometimes the neglect of the excavators has left them. This is perhaps a little-known example of the debunking of the most hackneyed aspects of the noble Roman past; it is a minor drama about the public vices of the ruling classes of the mid-Republican era which takes as its theme the infamous charges of embezzlement brought against Scipio Africanus, the greatest Roman hero of them all, who had already featured in Carmine Gallone's colossal *Scipio Africanus* (1937). The film mixes various archaeological settings, and makes the senate meet in a somewhat weedy Triangular Forum (a senate composed of men who speak a kind of caricature of 'Roman-speech') and locates the dwelling of a rather cynical Cato in the House of the Hanging Balcony. And it is still Pompeii, this time the Pompeii of the ruins, which makes its appearance in one of the most important scenes of the tortured existential journey of an English married couple in Roberto Rossellini's *Strangers (Viaggio in Italia)* (1953). The failure of the two characters to communicate and their different ways of coping with daily life reach a breaking point when they are confronted by the discovery of some skeletons from the 79 A.D. eruption, in a timeless moment which is only broken by the activities of the workmen who are observed from afar by the stern figure of Amedeo Maiuri. It is from this painful and buried past world that the slow journey of reconciliation begins leading to the lovers' final liberating embrace.

Coloured and animated by the music of one of the most popular groups of the 1970s, and enlivened by a film projection onto the ancient buildings showing spectacular old images of erupting volcanoes, the city appears in *Pink Floyd in Pompeii* (A. Maben, 1972). This film was intended to be a kind of psychedelic metaphor on the potential of minds enlarged by hallucinogenic experiences which were very much the fashion at that time, comparing the effects of a volcanic eruption on our perception of reality with those of an LSD trip. Looking back at this now, one is struck both by its ingenuous candour and the fact that it marks a first step in the history of cinema towards the videoclip, something which has occupied a considerable proportion of film production since the 1990s.

The golden age of Classical film ends in the mid-1960s; only a few were made after that and these were some of the most over-worked ones since the early days of cinema.

To finish the genre, we have films of an explicitly current-affairs slant: both Roberto Rossellini and Miklós Jancsó (*Agostino of Ippona* and *Rome Wants Another Caesar,* respectively, both produced in 1972) attempt to make a metaphorical analysis of the forces and contradictions inherent in moments of historical transition. Federico Fellini's wonderful imaginative *Satyricon* (1969), instead, is a film that stands on its own; it is a real mine of grotesque human types which he manages to insert into the fragmentary Petronian narrative by way of a profound analysis of the 'freedman culture' – which in many of his films from *La Dolce Vita* to *Voices of the Moon* – has been a means of understanding contemporary Italian society.

Both Rossellini's film and that of the Hungarian Jancsó have been broadcast on television, an indication that this kind of entertainment has passed from the large screen to that more recent and less inspiring mass medium, for which yet another (and particularly unfortunate) version of *The Last Days of Pompeii* (1984) has been made. It should be pointed out that television is to be credited with having produced the most original and refined version of *Quo Vadis?*, directed by Franco Rossi in 1985, who already made a name for himself with an unforgettable *Odyssey.* There is nothing conventional in this more recent version of Henryk Sienkiewicz's novel; the plot is based not so much on the clash between the empty pagan world and the living Christianity as on the friction between Nero and Petronius (played respectively by Klaus Maria Brandauer and a great Frederic Forrest) who are charged with portraying art's unrealistic aspiration to power and the measured power of art. What stands out is a scene in the darkness of the Domus Aurea, largely re-invented, but realistically so, when Nero turns his hand to building models of his new Rome, imagining it (as in the famous Tacitus passage) geometrically defined by streets and squares, like a great Hellenistic capital, and thus worthy to be called after the name of its new designer. What marks the film as different is the effort to put forward a plot and a setting far from any stereotypical vision of what is being represented; and for this reason, any inevitable reference to Rome, and thus also to Pompeii, is removed from this very cerebral version of *Quo Vadis?* This is where Pompeii has got to in Cinecittà and in Hollywood. But one cannot discount the possibility that the current distorted use of virtual reality, which mixes up past and present in an almost childish way, might end up by transforming Pompeii into a little Hollywood.

Beyond the Peplum*: Ridley Scott's* Gladiator

Twentieth-century film production ended as it began, with a historical movie studded with special effects. After an eclipse which lasted more than thirty years, a big American company, Universal, announced that a colossal set in ancient Rome would come out in 1999, directed by one of the most famous film-makers of the time, and starring a rapidly-rising actor. It seemed almost like a bet, to try to revive a production house which was evidently flagging, and which seemed only capable of providing repetitive action films, not to mention the enormous risks involved in reverting to a genre which appeared to have been extinct for some time. But the bet won in the end, also thanks to a particularly inspired publicity launch. *Gladiator* was the great commercial triumph of 2000, convincing even the sternest critics and carrying off five Oscars: best film, best leading actor, best costumes, best sound and, of course, best special effects. Nevertheless, what remains of the *peplum* and epic genres in this film, and what of the scenery to which the spectator of the 1960s had become accustomed? One can only point out the vast differences between the old and new kind of film. For one thing, the director is a well-known innovator. The Englishman Ridley Scott has profound knowledge of American cinema and above all its production techniques. He has shown himself capable of moving with ease and assurance through different genres, from historical films (*The Duellists*, 1977, *1492, The Conquest of Paradise*, 1992), science-fiction (*Alien*, 1979, *Blade Runner*, 1982), thrillers (*Black Rain*, 1989), road movies (*Thelma & Louise*, 1991) right through to horror-movies (*Hannibal*, 2001). *Gladiator*, too, perfectly fits this process of the reworking and redefinition of the cinema rules. One of the most significant innovations of the film is not so much the absolute invention of historical events which, like other films (the colossal *Fall of the Roman Empire*, 1964, and the second-rate *Two Gladiators*, 1964) leaves the real and historical facts of late second century A.D. out of account, so much as the deliberate avoidance of any conventional reconstruction of the Classical world. It would appear that the film lacks not only any attempt at creating a realistic background against which the characters can act – and thus any reference to an ancient city such as Pompeii or Herculaneum, (and it is worth mentioning that more than a hundred years pass between their destruction and the entirely fabricated fight between the loyal general Maximus and the treacherous Commodus) –

but it also lacks any reference to the place where the action is supposed to take place, namely Rome. In the rapid shots of the city, Rome always seems plunged into a yellowish gloomy shadow which blurs its outline (from which cupolas of Baroque churches, such as one sees from the Pincio gardens, also emerge) and among its monuments, piled one on top of the other, as in the far better-researched *Blade Runner* sets, the only really recognisable building is the Colosseum. And yet, it would not have been difficult to recreate the spaces as they actually were, as shown by the views afforded by the large and famous model created by Italo Gismondi. If you subtract from Rome what we know to be Rome, all you are left with is the vaguest idea of Rome – a city where impressive ancient remains live side by side with solemn Catholic churches – an idea held by the modern consumer of colossals and of organised tourist trips because it is at him, above all, that the film is aiming. Inside this framework, which cares little about the accuracy of Latin writing and frequently stumbles into vastly obvious narrative-ploys (such as, in order to stress the banal exercise of power by offering *panem et circenses*, making the bread distributed in the same place where the gladiators fought), the director has managed, however, to put in images and scenes, some crude and some sophisticated, which prompt the viewer's perception, and supply him with a much more accurate picture of the background against which the action was set than any strict Classical formula. A few examples may help make my meaning clearer. When Commodus' praetorian guards go to the general's estate in Spain to murder his family, the shot shows a long dusty road flanked by tall cypress trees, well-tended vineyards and above all, a big stone house surrounded by trees. There is no way we can recognise any element of the ancient countryside here; it was populated by villas arranged round vast colonnades and impressive and refined reception rooms, but the image evoked is nevertheless that of a *buen retiro*, a place to spend the rest of your life in peace. What better idea of this does modern man have than a *casale* in Tuscany? In contrast with this serene Spanish villa, Rome must appear in all its power and corruption; after a rapid panoramic sweep of its monuments, the only archaeological clue we have that we are actually in the city, the scene focusses on the triumph of Commodus, who to a fanfare of Wagnerian music, shows himself on the Capitol to receive the homage of a neatly ordered mob, drawn up in military rows, and gathered in a huge square which is surrounded by marble walls and colonnades.
It is not hard to see here an echo of the 'imperial' choreography of Nazi rallies, particulary that at Nuremberg in 1934 which was filmed by Leni Riefenstahl in her feature film *The Triumph of Will*. The very beginning of the film too, with its extraordinary battle between Romans and Germans, draws on the collective memory of the modern world. In this case, the details are more or less correct for the historical reconstruction; the weapons employed by the Roman artillery are by and large accurate reproductions of those which they actually used, like *balistae* from which stones or burning pitch were fired, or like the *scorpiones* used to catapult missiles weapons, described among others by Vitruvius.
It is the effect of a bombardment which puts one in mind of a modern scenario:

burning arrows shot from bows or fire-balls which strike panic into the ranks of the barbarians reproduce those scenes of bombing which are familiar to us all from media war-coverage, with skies furrowed by shell-fire and landscapes devastated by explosions. Other images are striking as quotations from other films. The savage African arena in which Maximus fights his first fights as a gladiator is highly reminiscent of the barbarous amphitheatre in the imaginary future world of *Mad Max Beyond Thunderdome* (1985) and the bloody duels are much indebted to the brutal battles of the comic-hero Conan (*Conan the Barbarian*, 1981). The incredible weapons used by the gladiators are not inspired by the collections displayed in archaeological museums all round the world (above all those in the National Museum in Naples), but by the weaponry of Japanese *manga* cartoons on which whole generations were raised during the 1980s and 1990s. These examples simply go to show how *Gladiator*, in its setting and subject matter, did not rely on more or less conventional reconstructions of the ancient world, but freed from any connection with the reality which it was supposed to represent, deliberately drew on the mythography of the world of cinema. Whether this constitutes the final glow of the sunset of *peplum* films – as happened for Westerns with Sam Peckinpah's magnificent *The Wild Bunch* (1969) – or does indeed prove a step forward towards a new way of imagining and reinventing the ancient world, only forthcoming Greco-Roman films will tell.

TALES FROM AN ERUPTION:
THE CONTEXT IN WHICH THE VICTIMS WERE FOUND

Tiziana Rocco   Herculaneum

"At Herculaneum, the water mixed and kneaded together all the great regurgitation from the jaws of the volcano, material both heavy and light, and made an infernal curdled mass, a river of sticky slime which rushed down and then came to a stagnant halt among the houses, and changed the whole sea coast first into a muddy marsh and then into a huge reef, and a vast, deep solidified promontory." (A. Maiuri, *Pompei e Ercolano tra case e abitanti*, Firenze 1958)

The two letters of Pliny the Younger sent to the historian Tacitus (Letters VI, 16, 20) provide a description of the events which occurred during the eruption of Vesuvius in August 79 A.D. Parallel analysis of the text of Pliny and of the archaeological and vulcanological data allow us to reconstruct the dynamics of the eruption at Herculaneum.
The city, located 7 kilometres to the west of Vesuvius, does not seem to have been hit, or only to a small degree, by the first phase of the eruption, which consisted of that rain of ash and pumice which violently descended on Pompeii and Stabia from about one in the morning on 24th August. The inhabitants of Herculaneum, although forewarned by the earth tremors and able to see the column of gas and pyroclastic material which was rising from Vesuvius, finally reaching a height of about 30 kilometres – the enormous cloud in the shape of a pine-tree as described by Pliny – dallied in the city, undecided as to what to do. Their flight probably began in the late afternoon, when the cloud reached a height which was sufficient to obscure the sun. About one o'clock in the afternoon of 25th August, the abrupt collapse of the column which had risen above the volcano led to the first deadly surge – a burning cloud of gas and ash (*nuée ardente*) reaching a temperature of about 400° – which hit Herculaneum in a few minutes, rolling along the sides of Vesuvius. The few inhabitants who were left in the city, maybe prevented from fleeing, died immediately. Up till now, excavations have only yielded thirty-two bodies of victims in the urban area – among which is a baby in a cradle – a suggestion that most of the five thousand inhabitants had abandoned the city. A few seconds after, the surge reached the beach area, where the approximately three hundred fugitives who had fled here to wait for the sea to calm down before attempting their flight were instantly killed. The first surge, followed by a pyroclastic flow, left a deposit of about 40–50 centimetres in the city and of 150 in the seafront area. About two in the morning, a second surge, of a lower temperature but swifter (30 metres/second) hit Herculaneum, damaging buildings and dragging with it a large amount of construction material, but by now every kind of life had been snuffed out. Four further surges followed before dawn, burying Herculaneum under 23 metres of volcanic material.
The way in which the city was buried, quite different from Pompeii, explains how, exceptionally, finds of an organic nature were preserved at Herculaneum, such as wood, elements of vegetation and even fibres of fabric, as well as the upper parts of the buildings.

THE VILLA OF THE PAPYRI

The Villa of the Papyri, one of the largest and most luxurious dwellings yet discovered in the Roman world, rose sheer above the sea, more than 250 metres in length. The building stretched out on various terraces descending towards the sea, making good use of its panoramic position and of the view of the bay. To give an idea of its enormous extent we need only remember that it had a huge peristyle with 25 × 100 columns, almost 100 metres long and 37 metres wide, and a swimming pool more than 66 metres long. In general, the plan of the villa consisted of an atrium that led onto a smaller peristyle, on the left of which was the *tablinum* or the living room, and on the right the eastern living quarters, with the library of papyri and the bath block, both yet to be entirely unearthed. From the *tablinum* one proceeded to the larger peristyle with its garden, onto which faced various rooms, and at the end, to a belvedere. The villa, situated about 25–30 metres below the current level of the city, immediately beyond the river which marked the western limit of Herculaneum, was discovered by chance in 1750 and until 1764 was partially excavated by the method of bore-holes and underground tunnels, at the same time as the other Vesuvian cities. The exploration system conducted by the Swiss construction engineer Weber, who left a plan marked with numerous annotations, was responsible for extensive damage to the wall structure, which was pierced in order to recover the rich works of art decorating the villa. Entire sculptural groups – fifty in bronze, twenty-one in marble – went to embellish the Real Museo at Portici, as well as mosaic floors and highly valuable fresco fragments, now preserved in the National Archaeological Museum in Naples. Equally important was the discovery of a library of papyri, which gave the villa its name. As many as 1758 scrolls were found, including texts of the Epicurean philosopher Philodemus of Gadar and some Latin texts, among which an 'Actian War' (*de bello Actiaco*). The exceptional collection of works of art can be attibuted to a rich proprietor from the late-Republican Roman *nobilitas*, a man of Epicurean leanings and of refined Hellenised culture, about whose identity several hypotheses have been put forward. The best known and most convincing sees the owner of the house as Lucius Calpurnius Piso Cesonius, the father-in-law of Julius Caesar and consul in 58 B.C. , or as his son, consul in 15 B.C. The other suggestion, which is perhaps better based, is that which identifies him as Appius Claudius Pulcher, the brother-in-law of Lucullus and consul in 38 B.C.: a friend of Cicero, he was known as a man steeped in Greek culture. Recently, the villa has been excavated again to bring to light and restore further parts of the building. This exploration, conducted by means of digging a deep narrow trench, has allowed to investigate the atrium area – decorated with polychrome mosaic floors with geometric motifs and Second-style paintings – as well as a colonnaded terrace facing the sea and located above the other rooms. Moreover, in one of the rooms of the lower floor that was flooded by the pyroclastic flow, a marble head of an Amazon of the so-called Sciarra type (fig. 1) was found, along with a statue of Hera (figs. 2, 3), a valuable marble copy of the Borghese type. These two sculptures are shown to the public for the first time, together with the sculptural groups which have already been exhibited at the National Archaeological Museum. [T. R.]

1. This marble head, broken at the base, is one of the best Roman copies of a type of Amazon of the Classical period, called 'Sciarra', attributed to the sculptor *Kresilas* or to Polyclitus.
SAP 80499
Mid-first century A.D.

2. Head of a statue of Hera; Roman marble copy of the so-called Borghese type, from the original by the sculptor Agoracritus, *c.* 430 B.C. The goddess is portrayed standing, wearing a peplos and himation SAP 81595

3. The statue of Hera at its discovery

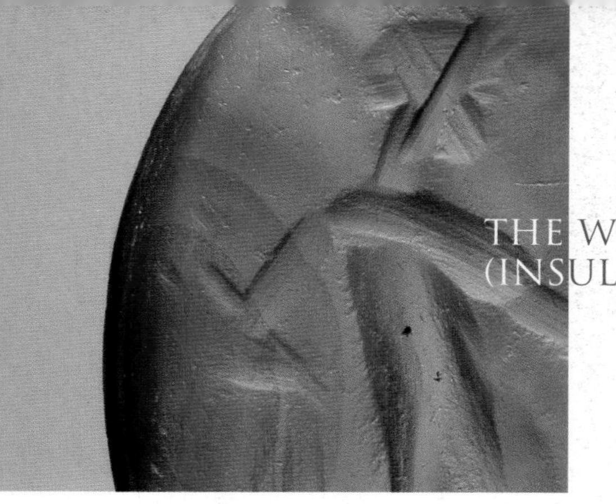

THE WORKSHOP OF THE GEMSTONE WORKER (INSULA ORIENTALIS II, 10)

Inside *Insula Orientalis* II, by and large taken up with the monumental complex of the Palaestra, buildings of a different type from those of the other regions of Herculaneum face outwards, towards the *cardo* V. Instead of grand houses or small workmen's dwellings, this area is occupied by big buildings with workshops and commercial premises on the ground floor, and *pergulae* and *coenacula* above, i.e. living-spaces with non of the usual elements of the traditional house, of the kind that were let out, in a manner which is also to be found in Ostia and Rome. In the 1958 edition of *Scavi Nuovi*, Amedeo Maiuri published the results of the excavations in this area between 1933 and 1937, focussing attention on the structures of 10 and 11, identifying the latter as a dyer's shop. In particular, he highlighted building 10 which, on the basis of the finds, was from then on known as the House of the Embroideress or the Workshop of the Gemstone Worker.
This is a workshop on the ground floor, divided into three rooms which can be identified as a kitchen, a cubicle (bedroom) and a backroom.
In the kitchen, as commonly found, was the *lararium*, near which an interesting little tufa altar was discovered, whose inscription indicates a domestic cult of Hercules. At the moment of excavation, the drama of the eruption became evident in all its brute force in the bedroom: a bed of carbonised wood with a high headboard, finely inlaid and veneered, had been lifted 70 centimetres from floor level by the mud, while on the floor was the upturned skeleton of an adolescent of about 15 years old who had tried to protect himself by hiding his head under the bed.
In the bedroom Maiuri also locates the discovery of a small hand-embroidery frame and a stool in carbonised wood, from which arose the romantic tale of the so-called embroideress' room.
In any case, M.P. Guidobaldi's recent reading of the excavation diaries established that these two artifacts did not belong to this building – their provenance being still unknown – thus undermining the story of the embroideress. The owner of the building may perhaps be identified from the large cache of gemstones and trinkets some of which were found in a little wooden box, others mostly in the backroom, a space evidently used for work purposes, to which some unearthed bronze instruments must have belonged. The discovery, among the numerous stones and trinkets of various materials, of two gemstones which were only roughly worked and not yet finished suggests that this was the workshop of a *gemmarius*, a kind of counter-less shop.
The Herculanean *gemmarius* who also had in his workshop a living area, produced, along with ordinary works (fig. 3) some highly refined artifacts as well, as can be seen from some of the gemstones that had been carved directly from imported matrices (figs. 4, 5).
A male portrait head with polychrome hair from the Augustan period was also found during the excavation; it was probably in the workshop for repairs which the *gemmarius* was never able to complete. [T.R.]

The Carving of Gemstones

"(Emeralds) alone among gemstones satisfy the gaze without glutting it." (Pliny, *Natural History*, XXXVII, 16)
From the end of the Republic and particularly after the conquest of Egypt, collecting and marketing gemstones became very fashionable, not only among the aristocracy but also among the new middle classes.
Concerns among right-thinking people that the abuse of jewels, whose precious materials such as gemstones were acquired outside Italy, would undermine the wealth of Rome found expression in the words of Tacitus: "What can I first of all suppress ... this really feminine madness, jewels, because of which our wealth is being handed over to foreign and hostile people" (*Annals*, III, 53). In cases where they had not been imported from abroad: but were locally worked, the stones must have originally come from abroad; emeralds from Egypt, amethysts and sardonyx from the East, jasper from Cyprus, cornelians generally from the mines in Noricum, pearls above all from India, Arabia and from the Egyptian coast of the Red Sea, amber from the Baltic states.
Two house-workshops of *gemmarii* are known in Pompeii – the House of Pinarius Cerialis and the House of the *Gemmarius* – but the workshop of the *Gemmarius* in Herculaneum is to date the only workshop yet known on the site. Tools found here, such as a stiletto and two pairs of pliers were certainly used for working gemstones. To work the stones, as we know, drills with points of varying shape and thickness were employed, reinforced with chips of hard stones or powdered diamond. For magnification, during the process of incision, phials of water were used and perhaps also lenses. [T. R.]

1. Detail of the well-preserved carbonised bed with its high headboard: the veneer is decorated with geometrical motifs of different kinds of woods SAP 81597 First century A.D.

2. Reconstruction of the bed with the decoration on the bedhead

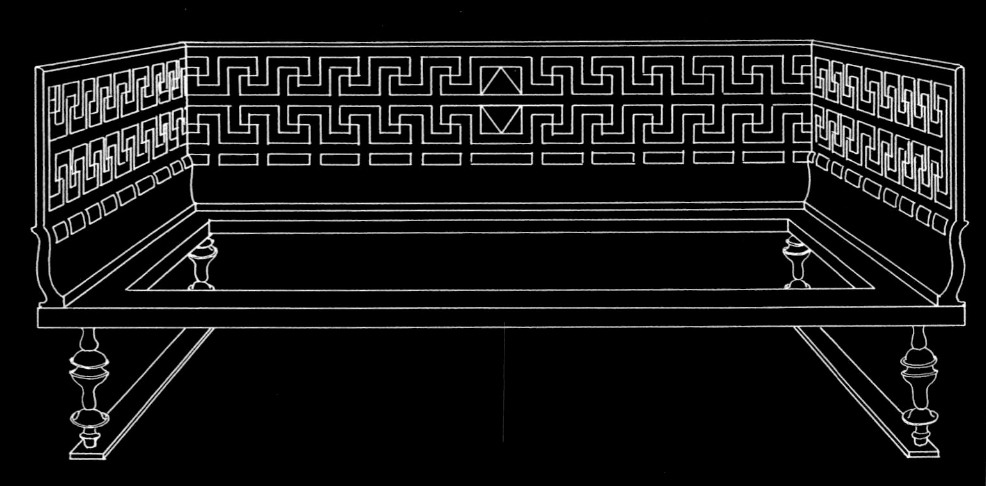

3. Engraving in cornelian with *Bonus Eventus (Agathodaimon)*
MANN 155884
First century A.D.

4. Engraving in glass paste with bust of a Maenad
MANN 155873
First century A.D.

5. Cameo in glass paste with bust of a man (a Hellenistic prince?) wearing a hat (*kausia*)
MANN 155881
First century A.D.

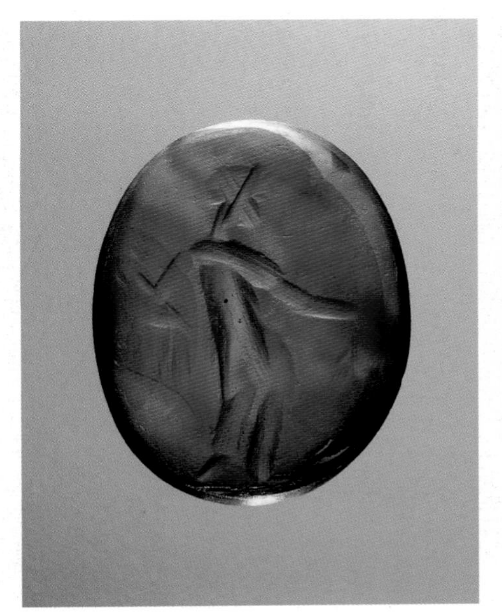

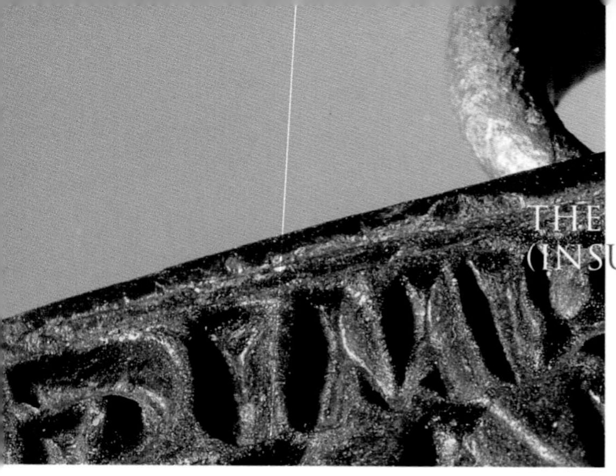

THE HOUSE OF M. PILIUS PRIMIGENIUS GRANIANUS (INSULA ORIENTALIS I, 1A)

The *Insula Orientalis* I is occupied by two grand houses only, the House of the Jewel and the House of the Relief of Telephus; although their atria open onto the front of *cardo* V, the buildings spread out in a north-south direction so that their terraces face the sea. Inside these dwellings a considerable number of people was found, who had obviously stayed in the city while the rest of the inhabitants had already abandoned Herculaneum.

They were discovered between 1934 and 1940 in some of the rooms on the lower floor of the House of the Jewel, once connected to it as a residential space within the same house, but later – perhaps after the construction of the Suburban Baths – detached in order to form a self-contained dwelling.

It is a small house, standing below that of the Jewel, and consisting of a long loggia – subsequently converted into a windowed *cryptoporticus* giving access onto other rooms – and some rooms hollowed out under the house above.

In 1935, in a room between the *vestibulum* and the alcove, a carbonised wooden chest was discovered, 80 centimetres above floor level. Apart from glass containers – a *simpulum*, a couple of small cups and two ointment jars – it held a bronze *signaculum*, or a signet-ring (fig. 1), which has given us the name of the last owner of the *domus: M. Pilius Primigenius Granianus.*

In 1940 the skeletons of a group of seven victims were found in one room of the house, the exedra, which obviously, by means of its location and of the wide opening onto the *cryptoporticus*, could give shelter to a large number of people. It is quite possible that these individuals were the inhabitants of the house, but in all likelihood, considering its location near the Harbour Gate, we may suppose that these large spaces could have offered a refuge to people trying to flee from the city towards the sea. Next to the skeletons a piece of cloth was also found containing nine engraved cornelians (fig. 2) and two bronze coins. The large square exedra, which was decorated with a mosaic floor, also housed a small circular three-legged wooden table, the legs in the form of greyhounds, probably used for meals (fig. 3).

A wooden rocking cradle (fig. 4) was also found in the house, with the barely-recognisable traces of a baby lying on a little fibre mattress. Amedeo Maiuri, who discovered it, has made this find famous, describing it in dramatic terms: "In one of these rooms a wooden cradle was found, one of those rocking cradles which for centuries has preserved, in the form and outline of its wooden slats, the basic shape imposed by the use and function it must serve, namely to calm a baby's crying and sooth it to sleep. Inside this cradle were the barely-recognisable traces of a little skeleton ... The wretched mistery of this abandoned cradle hangs over the house of M. Pilius Primigenius Granianus." [T. R.]

1. Bronze signet-ring used to seal the owner's documents and legal writings. *M. Pilius Primigenius Granianus*
SAP 76609
First century A.D.

2. Engraving in *prasium* with Eros or Erotes on a dolphin, found along with eight cornelians in a piece of cloth near some victims in the exedra
MANN 158863
First century A.D.

The Wood of Herculaneum

The way in which Herculaneum was buried, different from that of Pompeii, meant that wooden objects were exceptionally well preserved and have come down to us because they were enveloped in solidified pyroclastic material.
There are numerous articles of wooden furniture preserved at Herculaneum: beds – almost all with high headboards – six small tables – all round-shaped apart from one which is crescent-shaped – fourteen cupboards – four of which are *lararia* – a stool, a box and a cradle. Nothing remains of the other pieces of furniture, for example of the chairs and wooden boxes mentioned in the eighteenth- and nineteenth-century excavation reports, because of the lack of reinforcement construction at the time they were excavated. Silver fir seems to have been the most commonly used wood in the area round Vesuvius, partly produced in Campania and partly imported from the Alps.
Besides various different qualities of wood, the cabinet makers of Herculaneum used various other materials to decorate furniture, such as bronze, particularly for beds, bone for hinges and glass paste for inlay on the feet of small tables. The use of dove-tailed joints and framed panels in the furniture reveals a high standard of crafstmanship among the local artisans. [T. R.]

3. Small table
in carbonised wood,
with a circular top,
supported by three
curved legs, ending
in greyhounds' paws,
designed
for the consumption
of food
SAP 77333
First century A.D.

4. Baby's rocking
cradle in carbonised
wood, with
six transverse slats,
on which a small
fibre mattress
was placed
SAP 78444
First century A.D.

THE ANCIENT SEAFRONT AND THE ARCADES ON THE BEACH OF HERCULANEUM

The excavations conducted in the 1980s of the area in front of the suburban part of Herculaneum, starting from the Suburban Baths, uncovered the entire shoreline, consisting of a beach with black sand and rocks. In the stretch in front of the beach some arcades were also discovered – vaulted rooms under the terrace above – used partly to store the boats (with wooden doors), and partly as an outlet for the drains. After the casual discovery of one skeleton in 1980, many more were found, reaching a total of almost three hundred, as well as some dogs and two horses. As a result, the previously held theory that the people of Herculaneum had managed to save themselves and get away, a hypothesis based on the scarcity of human remains found until then, was rapidly discounted.
This large number of skeletons was discovered inside an ash-heap 1.50 centimetres deep that was deposited by the *nuée ardente* (surge 1) which hit Herculaneum at about one in the morning of 25th August. The eruption, which started in the late morning of 24th August with the emission of a cloud in the shape of a pine-tree shot up high into the atmosphere over the crater, does not appear to have reached Herculaneum until the evening of 24th August, as witnessed by the lack of volcanic material. Nevertheless, the phenomenon, made worse by the explosions and the earth tremors which doubtlessly accompanied it, gave a clear signal to the town inhabitants, who up till then had been rather slow or had underestimated the danger; in all likelihood, they seriously considered abandoning the city only in the late afternoon, as the light failed. The element of timing is confirmed by the lamps found by many fugitives, which makes one think that the flight took place in darkness. In any case, it is probable that each person, in the uncertainty as to whether to leave his or her house or to stay, would have had the time to take or to wear his/her most valuable possessions, ones which could be carried – such as coins, necklaces and objects of value – as can be seen from the articles found near or on the victims. Although some of the inhabitants would doubtless have made their way towards cluttered land routes, it would have been clear to all those who had waited in the city until late afternoon that the only means of escape was by sea, in the opposite direction to the danger. The fugitives reached the beach along a road which led to a narrow, rugged tunnel, and from this, down a sheer staircase, to a steep slope.
It is generally maintained that the flight towards the sea, although fast, was not panicked but on the contrary, rather orderly, as no victims have been found at the most difficult points on the route, such as the entrance to the tunnel or the steep descent. Even though there were old people and several children, (the latter probably carried in their mothers' arms), they were evidently able to negotiate the downhill slope, even in the darkness, without encountering difficulties of any sort. We cannot know how many people from Herculaneum, out of a population numbering about five thousand, actually managed to reach the beach, but in all likelihood many of them (some thousand) got away – although there is no evidence as to whether they were able to reach safety – embarking on little fishing boats which must have been moored on the shore or on the moles of the former seafront, as we can tell from the remains of ropes, hooks and other bits of fishing tackle. In any case, approximately three hundred people had remained on the beach, and only one small boat – which was found upturned – when, around one o'clock in the morning of 25th August, the coastline of Herculaneum was hit by the first *nuée ardente* (surge 1). The darkness and the disparity

of levels between the city, from which the surge came, and the beach, as well as the presence of a containing wall, doubtless prevented the fugitives sheltering here from seeing the deadly cloud in advance, although its arrival would have been heralded by flashes of light and loud noise.
The effects of the first cloud, which in the course of a few minutes produced a deposit of fine ash 1.50 metres deep, were devastating and held out no hope of survival. Those who found themselves on the beach were hurled to the ground, as one can tell from the prone or supine position of the skeletons – killed instantly, probably due to ebullition and evaporation of their organic liquids, or in some cases perhaps to the explosion of their skulls, by the surge which had reached a temperature of 400° C. Those who were in the arcades, and were not directly exposed to the high temperatures of the surge, died slowly, due to shock and burns and asphyxiated by the dust from the cloud, as one can tell from their crouching position. The objects found near the people in the excavations carried out on the former shoreline level and in the arcades looking out over it, along with the paleo-biological and paleo-pathological analyses conducted on many of the skeletons, in many cases help reconstruct the stories and identities of the fugitives, and an interesting selection of these is presented in the exhibition.
Many of them were carrying their most valuable possessions: house keys, splendid jewels, signet-rings, baskets and bags with coins, money-boxes, amulets, and tools of their trades, for example fisherman's hooks.

Arcades 7 and 8
The skeletons of these arcades were positioned mostly towards the back walls, at a level varying between 20 and 30 centimetres from the floor.
The largest group of objects discovered near the skeletons of Arcades 7 and 8 are coins and necklaces, worn or kept in little containers, which give us valuable information about articles of feminine adornment in the Vesuvius area during the first century A.D.
Particularly interesting is the discovery in Arcade 7 of a cup of chalcedonic agate (fig. 1) near the skeleton of a woman who was wearing a necklace made up of different stones, with beads in the shape of amulets (fig. 2). In addition to this, the hoard of gold jewellery found in Arcade 8 is very significant because it constitutes the most considerable and valuable find to date in the Herculaneum area.
It consists of a gold *catena* 180 centimetres long (fig. 3) – which was worn on the body, tight at the waist and crossed over the chest and shoulders – two bracelets with hemispheres (fig. 4), five gold rings with gemstones (fig. 5), a pair of earrings with river-pearls, as well as containers and silverware, found between two skeletons, wrapped up in a cloth inside a little wooden box. On another female skeleton a couple of armbands were found, together with two rings (fig. 6) and a gold ornament.

Arcades 11 and 12
In Arcade 11, besides gold and silver jewellery, a large number of objects was found next to the fugitives, among which were a lamp (fig. 7) – obviously useful to light up the darkness of those dramatic hours – three small silver spoons (fig. 8), and a wicker basket laden with a large amount of silver and bronze coins, now welded together (fig. 9).
The basket found near one of the victims is of exceptional interest, constituting as it does the average savings of a citizen of Herculaneum at the moment of the eruption. On the skeletons nearest to the door of the arcade, many traces of carbonised fabric, linen or woolen clothing have further been noted, with which the fugitives were probably trying to protect themselves.
The excavation of Arcade 12, instead, has yielded thirty-two skeletons from

which a cast has been made of the whole room (fig. 10), and which gives a note of high drama to the exhibition.
Among the victims, divided into twenty adults, three young people, two children and seven babies, one adult stands out. Near him a wooden box was found containing a complete set of surgical instruments (figs. 11, 12), obviously connected to the occupation of the fugitive, who can be identified as a doctor. Before abandoning everything, he had tried to salvage the tools of his trade. The surgical instrument box, divided inside into four compartments, has an iron hinge on one side for easy opening. A strip of slate had been inserted into the lid, while inside there were bronze cylindrical containers and various bronze and iron surgical instruments for making incisions, cutting and sewing wounds: six lancets and scalpels, a forceps (*volsella*), two small hooks (*hamuli*), a probe, a needle (*acus*) and a small case.
In particular, the bronze probe, shaped like a small stick with its end flattened in the form of a leaf, served to mix and apply medicaments. The medical instruments, found along with other objects (mostly jewellery and coins) in Arcade 12, which are so similar to modern ones, offers an interesting example of the high level of Roman surgery.

The Ancient Seafront
Among the victims found on the ground of the ancient seafront, a rather tall person (about 1.80 metres in height) appears to be most significant. From the objects he was carrying, it is possible to identify him as a soldier: he was wearing a big belt at his hip level, from which hung a *gladius* (sword) (fig. 13) and a dagger (figs. 14, 15) with silver *cingula,* and on his shoulders he had a bag – a sort of backpack – with two chisels, an awl, and a small iron hammer. At his side was also found a hoard of gold and silver coins, which had probably been contained in a bag. The find of three aurei and fifteen silver denarii, comprising a total value of 360 sesterces, is interesting as it indicates not only that soldiers were quite well off – we know they were paid in silver coinage and that they received bonuses which increased their low pay rate – but also a willing and a possibility to hoard up. As we have no evidence for military detachments in the area, we can put forward the theory that this soldier belonged to the fleet at Cape Misenum and that he was caught short, for reasons unknown, in the area of the eruption.
A great quantity of gold jewellery was furthermore found by the body of a woman on the beach: snake-shaped armbands (fig. 16), two rings and a pair of gold earrings. [T. R.]

1. This small drinking cup in chalcedonic agate, with rounded rim and deep interior, is among the rare objects in semi-precious stone found in the Vesuvius area
SAP 78969
First century A.D.

2. Necklace beads in amber, cornelian, onyx, chalcedony, agate, lead, bronze, glass, bone, mother-of-pearl, rock-crystal and shells. The presence of trinkets in the form of amulets indicates an apotropaic use of the necklace
SAP 78968
First century A.D.

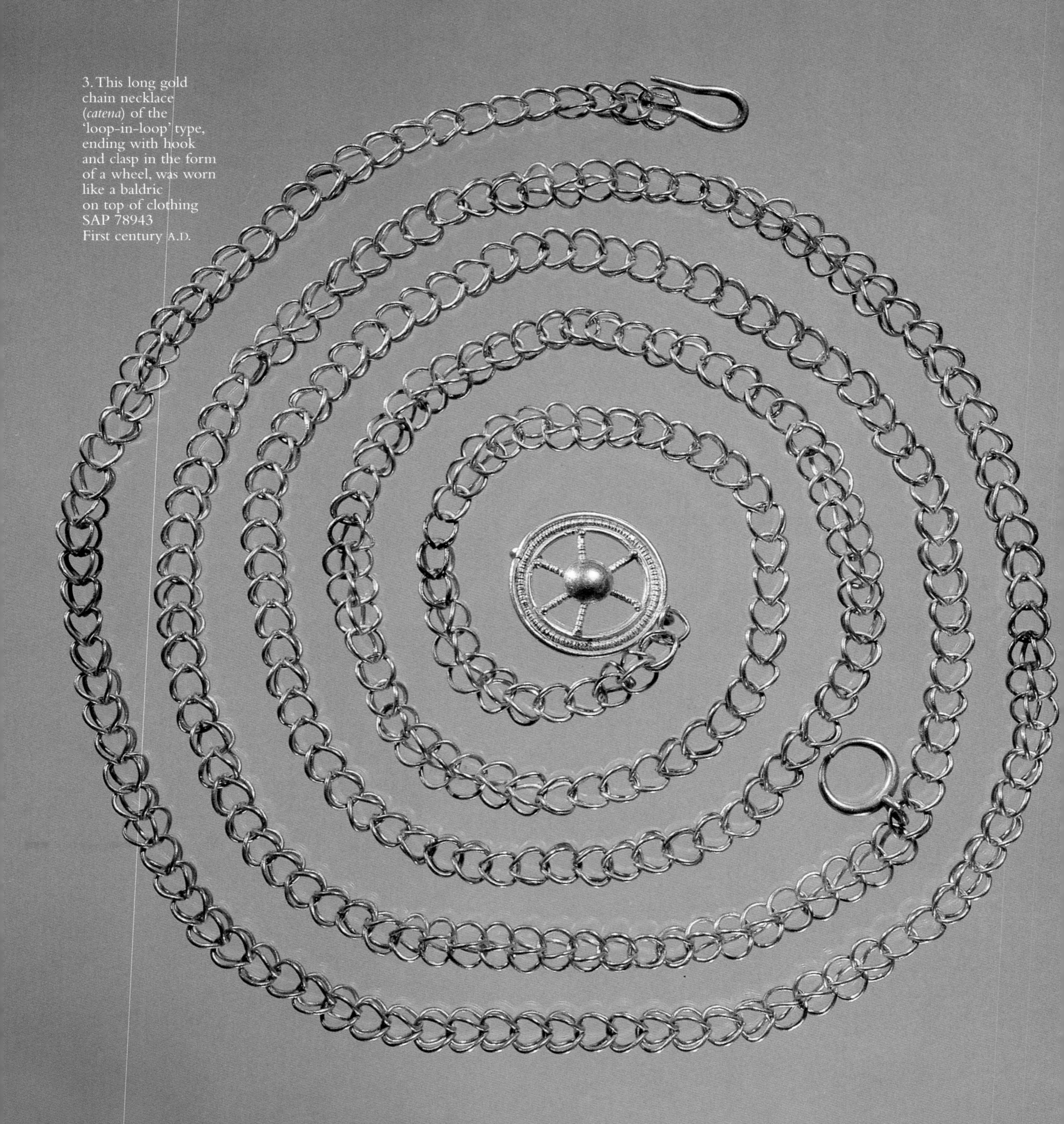

3. This long gold chain necklace (*catena*) of the 'loop-in-loop' type, ending with hook and clasp in the form of a wheel, was worn like a baldric on top of clothing
SAP 78943
First century A.D.

4. Pair of armbands with gold hemispheres, of a type quite common in the Vesuvius area
SAP 78944–78945
First century A.D.

5. Gold ring set with a cornelian. The gemstone shows an incised winged Nemesis who is holding a snake and a *patera*
SAP 78948
First century A.D.

6. Gold ring set with a chalcedonic sardonyx, bearing the incision of a bird of prey facing right
SAP 78970
First century A.D.

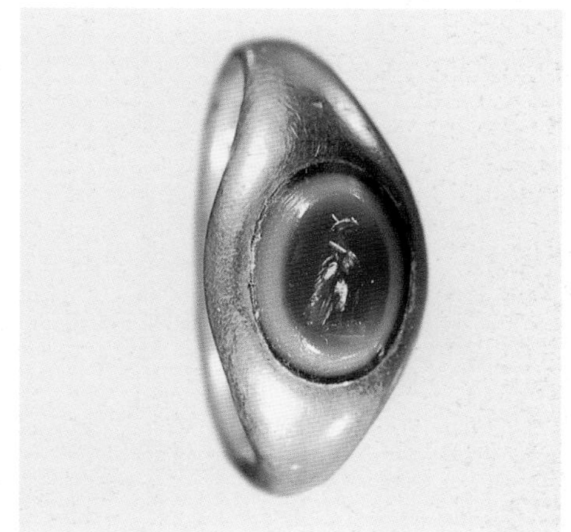

8. Three small silver spoons found in Arcade 11, piled on top of each other near two skeletons
SAP 78578
Flavian period

7. Bronze lamp with handle ending in swan's head found in Arcade 11
SAP 78635
Flavian period

9. Wicker basket laden with a great number of silver and bronze coins
SAP 78675
Flavian period

The Casts of the Victims

The first sculpture and inscription casts were made in Pompeii as early as the nineteenth century: a cast of a door, in fact, goes back to 1856.
The idea of applying this method to human bodies as well was introduced by Fiorelli in February 1863: by pouring plaster into the cavities left by the bodies in the ash, it became clear that one could reproduce faithful images of the victims, caught in the final and most dramatic moment of their lives.
In 1984, when making a cast of the girl found in the villa at Oplontis, the plaster was replaced by transparent epoxy resin, because of its possibilities of showing the bones and other things found in the body cavities; however, this choice does not appear to have been altogether felicitous and has not been used subsequently.
The cast of the fugitives of Arcade 12 at Herculaneum, currently on display, is instead an example of modern technology. Here we have an 'archeo-surface' cast, quite large and highly detailed, which has been achieved with the aid of silicon elastomer, a material which ensures an extremely faithful copy. [T. R.]

10. Detail of the 'archeo-surface' of Arcade 12, with the skeletons of the fugitives SAP n.n.

11. Surgeon's implements found in Arcade 12: slate slab on the left; bronze surgical instruments in the centre; cylindrical bronze cases for the implementon on the right SAP 78999–79000 Flavian period

12. Detail of the surgeon's set of instruments: the bronze cylindrical cases in various sizes (diam. 2/3 cms) SAP 78999–79000

13. Soldier's *gladius* with iron handle and wooden sheath, perhaps covered in leather, on which two silver rivets from the sword-belt are visible
SAP 79093
First century A.D.

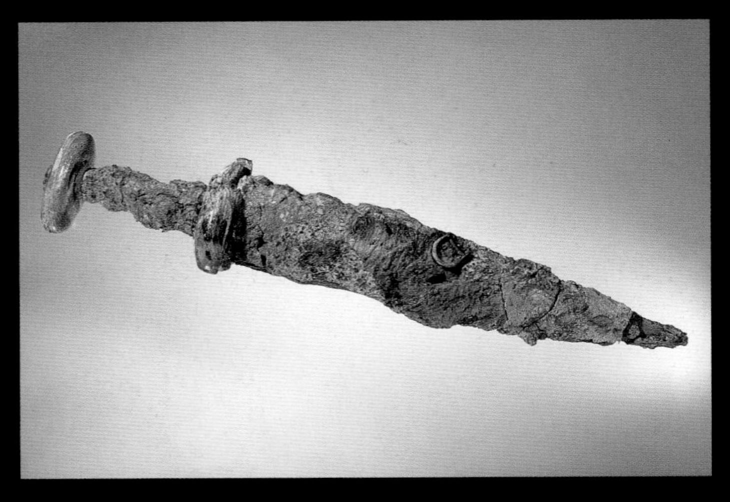

14, 15. Soldier's iron dagger with bone handle and wooden sheath, perhaps covered in leather, and detail of the relief decoration
SAP 79094
First century A.D.

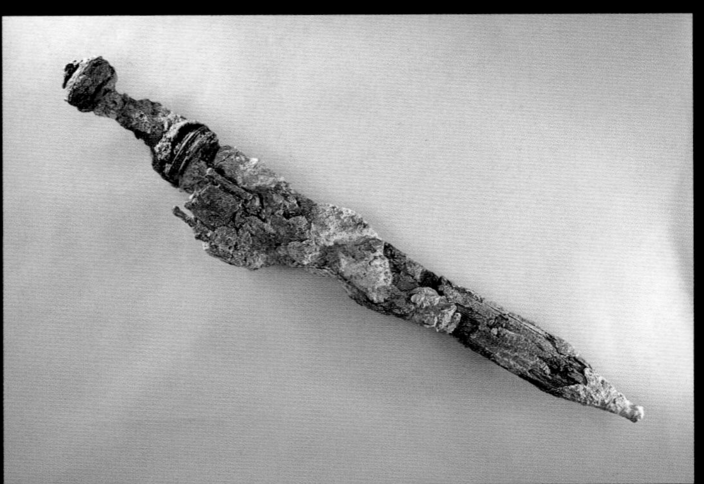

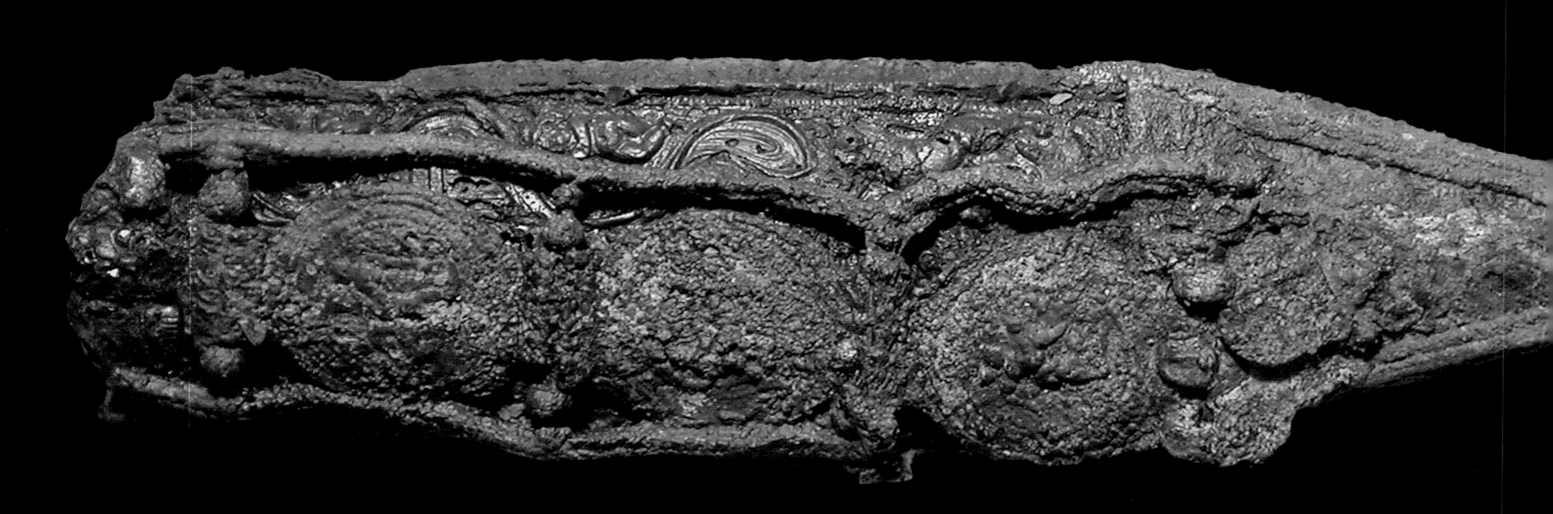

16. Pair of snake-shaped bracelets in gold and glass paste
SAP 78358
First century A.D.

Anna Civale Oplontis

The geographer Strabo describes the Campanian coast between Misenum and Sorrento as a single large city because of the almost continuous succession of villas and coastal settlements. Among these, the *Tabula Peutingeriana* – a road map of the Roman empire – records the site of Oplontis, located approximately 5 kilometres from Pompeii, in the modern town of Torre Annunziata.
Systematic excavations between 1964 and 1984, have brought to light two villas in the area of Mascatelle – a sumptuous residence (Villa A) attributed to *Poppaea Sabina*, second wife of the Emperor Nero, and an agricultural establishment (Villa B), perhaps the property of *Lucius Crassius Tertius*. Along with the baths which were discovered at Punta Oncino in 1834, these villas help us to define Oplontis as a town of medium size on the outskirts of Pompeii, under its administration but nevertheless with enough infrastructure of its own to suggest a well-equipped residential area.
Its inhabitants died at about one o'clock in the morning of 25th August with the first of the surges – those glowing avalanches of volcanic material moving very quickly – which killed all those who had not yet managed to get out of the area where the eruption was happening.
In the previous few hours, the winds which had been blowing hard in a south-east direction had caused a dense rain of pumice to fall on the coastal area; at first it was white, then grey, and as it accumulated it was responsible for the collapse of many roofs and caused many people to seek refuge in the so-called Villa of *Lucius Crassius Tertius*; others, probably had managed to reach the beach, hoping in vain to escape via the sea.

THE VILLA OF LUCIUS CRASSIUS TERTIUS

The villa, which lies close to the more famous Villa of Poppaea, is attributed to *Lucius Crassius Tertius*, who belonged to a *gens* of servile origin which established itself, both politically and economically (fig. 1) in the years before the eruption. This two-storey structure – partially excavated between 1974 and 1991 – can be dated to the late second century B.C. and occupies a large *insula*, bounded to the north by a road lined with various shops.
It is not a luxurious house: for the most part the rooms are not even plastered, or in some cases, are whitewashed and have a simple beaten earth floor. A peristyle with a double row of columns surrounds a courtyard of beaten earth, flanked by various rustic-type rooms used for manufacturing purposes. Other rooms, maybe storerooms, opened onto another portico, of which only a few columns remain.
The upper floor, instead, was entirely given over to the living quarters of the *dominus*.
This is a case of a small business which produced wine, oil and other agricultural produce. Evidence of this comes from the discovery, in the four sides of the peristyle and in some nearby rooms, of piles of amphorae (more than four hundred), upturned and piled one upon another, maybe intended to store aromatic wine.
This commercial activity is further confirmed by a series of weights (fig. 2) used for sorting and selling the merchandise.
As many as seventy-four fugitives had taken refuge in one of the rooms of the villa. Here they died, at one o'clock in the morning of 25th August, partly from the surge which hit Oplontis, and partly from the collapse of the vault covered by volcanic debris. In the first phase of the eruption, when the pyroclastic material began to infiltrate from outside, this group crowded deep into the room (fig. 3). Subsequently, the collapsing of the roof and the infiltration of volcanic material – which also tore a hole in the ceiling – drove those who were still alive back to the entrance. Before their asphyxiation and death, they tried to climb up onto the heap of detritus and corpses.
It is impossible to ascertain whether they were inhabitants of the villa or fugitives heading towards the sea.
The skeletons can be divided into two groups, one without artifacts, the other comprising people with jewels and money on them.
In the first group we may perhaps identify people belonging to a social class which was not well-off, perhaps the craftsmen employed in commercial production.
In the second group we find skeletons with jewellery, either on them, or nearby, concealed in their clothing or stashed in appropriate containers (fig. 4) The women – like skeleton 14 – were wearing a complete *parure* of jewellery (figs. 5, 6) – or like skeleton 10 (fig. 7) – a rather simpler set comprising a ring, an armband and a hairpin. Next to skeleton 7, maybe that of a woman, a hoard of coins was found in a canvas bag laid carefully at her side (fig. 8); this consisted of four hundred and nine gold, silver and bronze coins, of a overall value of 1062 sesterces. She is not a *domina,* she does not have jewels with her, though she possesses a considerable amount of money, perhaps pertaining to the commercial activity which went on in that building.
Skeleton 27 has been tentatively identified as the owner of the villa: he had with him silverware, jewels (fig. 9) and coins amounting to 10.000 sesterces, the highest overall sum found in the Vesuvius area. The coins were partly stashed in a little box, along with some pieces of silverware and jewels (the family valuables?), and partly in a bag which has since dissolved (personal belongings?) and which must originally have been held at the top of the thorax. [A. C.]

1. Strongbox found in the peristyle of the house, equipped with feet and made of a wooden casing, on which thin sheets of iron were laid – fixed with large studded nails – and made stronger by further reinforcement strips
SAP 85179
First century B.C.

2. Circular-shaped ten pound weight (*decapondium*) with traces, on the upper surface, of a moving iron handle soldered in lead. It is inscribed with the letters AVT, and, on the other side, presumably the letter C
SAP 73225
First century A.D.

3. Some of the skeletons driven to the back of the room by the impact of the eruption

4. Leather bag in numerous fragments, with gold decoration
SAP 85180
First century A.D.

Women's Jewellery

If the only piece of jewellery permitted to men – as a sign of distinction and wealth – was the ring, the articles of jewellery which made up a woman's *parure* were very varied. Hair was held back by diadems and gold nets, bound with *vittae* (hairbands) or secured by hairpins with a variety of differently shaped clasps.

Necklaces (*monilia*) were of varying lengths: as well as longer ones consisting solely of gold chains with vine-leaf pendants, there were also shorter ones of just pearls or gold chains of different designs linking emeralds, pearls or glass paste. Necklaces with a broad band were rarer. Occasionally, necklaces were hung with amulets, often in the form of crescents or wheels. In addition, there were longer 'bust' necklaces (*catenae*) with rather intricate chains which rested on the shoulders and then came down as far as the hips, fastened on the chest and the back with two bosses where it crossed over. These examples have a 'loop-in-loop' type chain, cut from gold foil or in a string of loops; the bosses are smooth, with a virtually plain border.

Rings, worn several at a time, had narrow bands with circular bezels or wide bands with curved ones. They bore engraved seal stones, or cameos of a purely decorative function; sometimes they took the form of snakes or were simple little circles bearing pearls or small uncut emeralds.

Among the earrings, the most common type was that of the small pendant in the form of a small vessel, or quarter-shape sphere, in gold leaf, sometimes embellished with coloured stones set into the metal or little beads soldered onto the surface.

There are many earrings in the form of bunches of grapes, with pearls, emeralds and gold spheres hanging from a gold wire, or of the pendant type, with pearls threaded onto the ends of two or three sections of gold, hanging from a horizontal clip.

Armbands were also in fashion (*armillae*): they were in the shape of two or more narrow snakes. Fastening bracelets were also very common, with gold hemispheres linked by small rings with little shells or leaves, in single or double rows.

[A. C.]

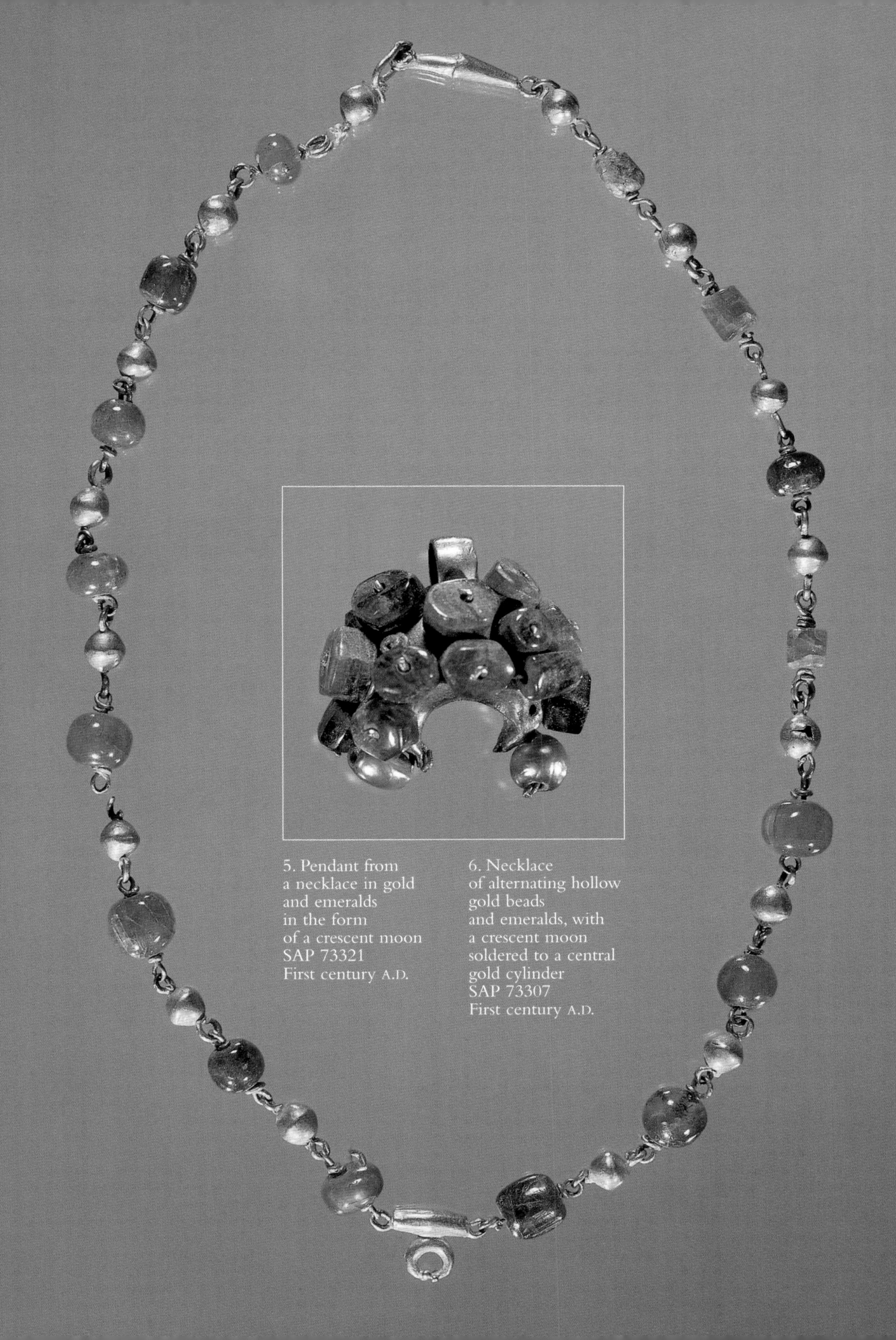

5. Pendant from a necklace in gold and emeralds in the form of a crescent moon
SAP 73321
First century A.D.

6. Necklace of alternating hollow gold beads and emeralds, with a crescent moon soldered to a central gold cylinder
SAP 73307
First century A.D.

7. A new experimental technique was used in 1984 to make this cast of a young girl. The moment it was excavated, a wax cast was taken from the cavity left by her decomposed body. From this a plaster mould was then taken, and another cast made by pouring in transparent epoxy resin, which has the advantage, unlike the traditional plaster method, of revealing not only the internal bone-structure of the person, but also any objects they had on them

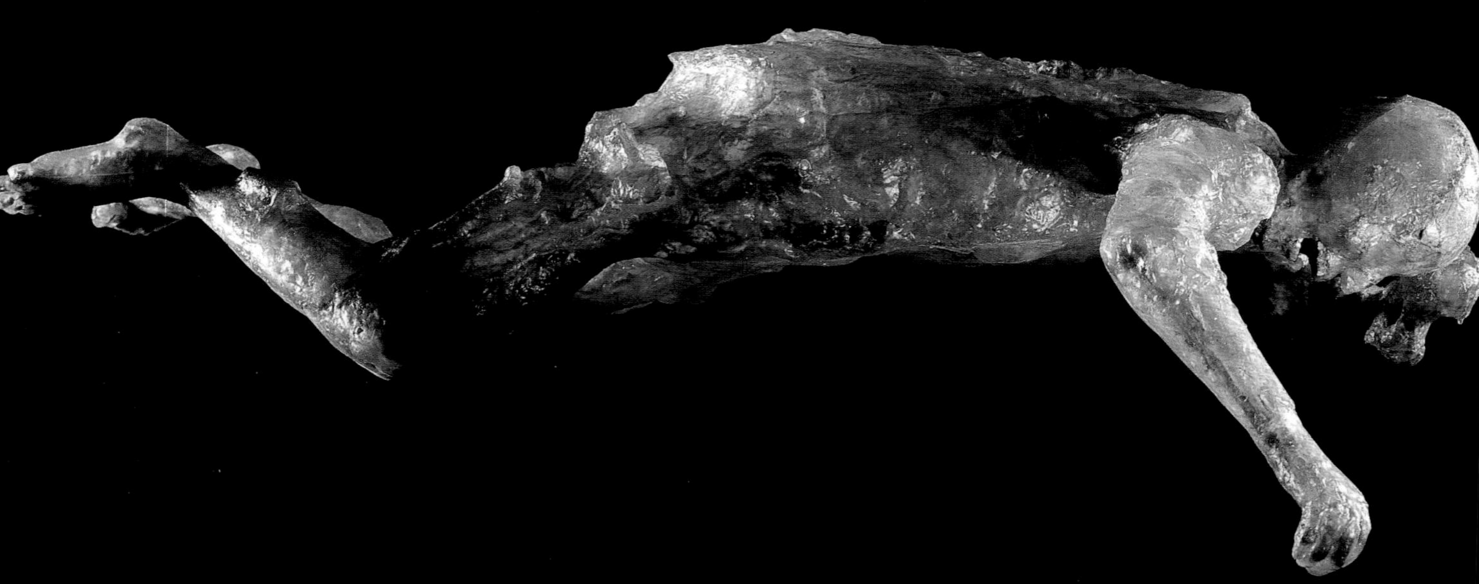

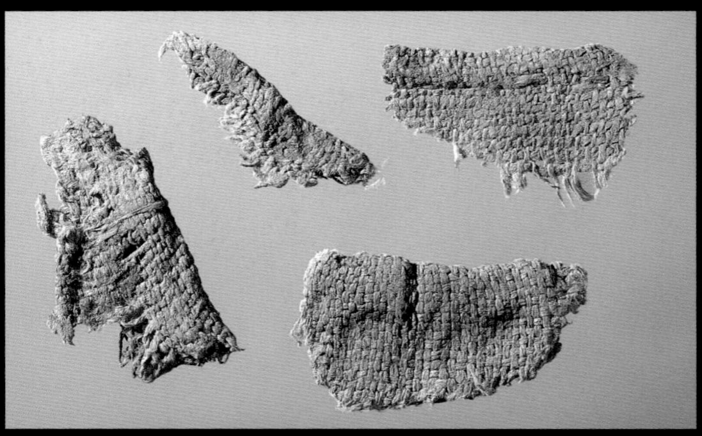

8. Four fragments of coarsely woven cloth similar to canvas SAP 73305 First century A.D.

8. *Catena* formed by pairs of thin chains of the 'loop-in-loop' type and two bosses with hemispherical segments
SAP 73410
First century A.D.

Anna Civale Terzigno

In antiquity the land on the slopes of the south-east side of Vesuvius – today the town of Terzigno – formed the furthest northern outskirts of Pompeii. From the 1980s onwards, extraction of volcanic material from the quarries in Boccia al Maura, about 6 kilometres distant from Pompeii, have revealed three residential sites, provisionally named Villa 1, Villa 2 and Villa 6, built on a north-south axis, perhaps near the road which must have led from Pompeii to Nola. The structure of the rooms, the presence of *torcularia* and of wine cellars, as well as the sorrounding farmland, have allowed us to identify these buildings as some of the numerous farms, devoted mainly to wine-producing, which were common in the area.
The initial phase of the eruption in this area, which was nearest to the volcano, consisted of a fall of greyish ash at about one in the afternoon on 24th August and which must have caused alarm among the inhabitants who were going about their daily business. The ash cloud, which was by now obscuring the sun, the continuous earth tremors, and the deafening noises coming from the volcano would have provoked anxiety and fear, and driven the farm workers to return in haste to the farms; some would have decided to seek refuge in Pompeii or, most likely, to flee to the nearby shore of Oplontis.
During the day, the rain of ash, pumice and incandescent volcanic particles continued without respite, settling on the roofs and serving to undermine the stability of the houses. About eight in the evening, the eruption took a further abrupt turn, in the form of the first surges which affected the eastern areas nearest to Vesuvius. In the night between 24th and 25th August, at some point between one and two o'clock, the Terzigno area was hit by a cloud of pyroclastic material and heated gas (*nuée ardente*), the second to come from Vesuvius, which completed the destruction and almost instantaneously killed those who had not managed to escape.

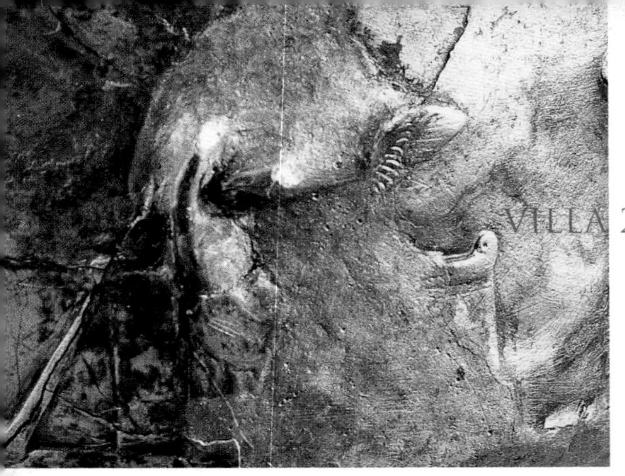

VILLA 2

In the spring of 1984, the find of a group of skeletons with golden jewellery, silverware and silver coins, turned what had started as the simple excavation of the top of a wall, into the investigation of a far more extensive area, bringing to light this property of both residential and manufacturing purposes, which has still not been fully excavated.
The central area was a courtyard with porticoes on two sides, flanked by rooms used either for the production and storage of wine or for living purposes. The southern wing of the building where the wine was produced, had the *torcularium*, with its service area, and the wine cellar which has yielded, in varying states of preservation, twenty-four *dolia* – of varying cubic capacities and with traces of ancient repairs, indicating that they had been in use for a long time – embedded in the soil up to the neck (*dolia defossa*) and arranged in parallel rows with walkways in between.
The farm buildings were to the north: a living room (A), a big kitchen and other service rooms opened onto the portico of the central courtyard.
To the east of the villa was a vast terraced area, about 600 square metres, used as a *hortus* and watered by a circular-opening cistern.
We can probably identify the inhabitants of the villa as a group of five people, accompanied by two dogs, whose skeletons were found in the heap of ash which had accumulated uniformly in the room (A).
The surge hit them without warning, rendering their attempt at flight useless, and the buildings, knocked down by the force of the eruption, collapsed upon their now lifeless bodies.
Skeletons I, II and III were found stretched out just by the door; skeleton IV was found a bit further away, but equally heading towards it. Skeleton V, next to which were the skeletons of the dogs, was even further away from the door and had his back turned to it, curled up with his hands in front of his face, painfully resigned to a tragic death beside his life-long friends.
Only three of the bodies were found with coins on them; but if skeletons I and V were only carrying their meagre savings, adequate for day-to-day expenses, skeleton III bore a little hoard of treasure, which, along with the quality and quantity of objects found with it, leads one to suspect that they belonged to the young *domina* who, when the catastrophe occurred, along with her *familia* of slaves, tried to take refuge in what seemed the safest place in the house, while waiting to make a final escape out to the countryside.
The woman, who was presumably young, had tried to take with her dearest and most valuable personal objects: in addition to the hoard of coins – twenty-one Republican and Imperial denarii – which must have constituted her own savings, there were jewels and silverware. Next to her skeleton three gold necklaces (figs. 1–3) were found, maybe actually worn, and at a little distance, a pair of bracelets, likewise in gold, which the woman was probably holding.
Near the young woman a little amphora and a mirror (fig. 4) were discovered, pieces of *argentum balneare* which she had taken with her. Scattered along the portico, on what must have been the path of the victims' flight, and lost as they fled, a splendid silver drinking service was found, comprising a pair of *skyphoi* (fig. 5) and a *situla* (ladle) – silverware of valuable make and outstanding elegance, which along with the *argentum balneare*, bears witness to the good taste and social level of the anonymous family who owned this villa. Likewise, the horses' harnesses show unusual decorative elements, as we see in the bronze *falera* with a small silver-embossed head of a woman found in the portico as well. [A. C.]

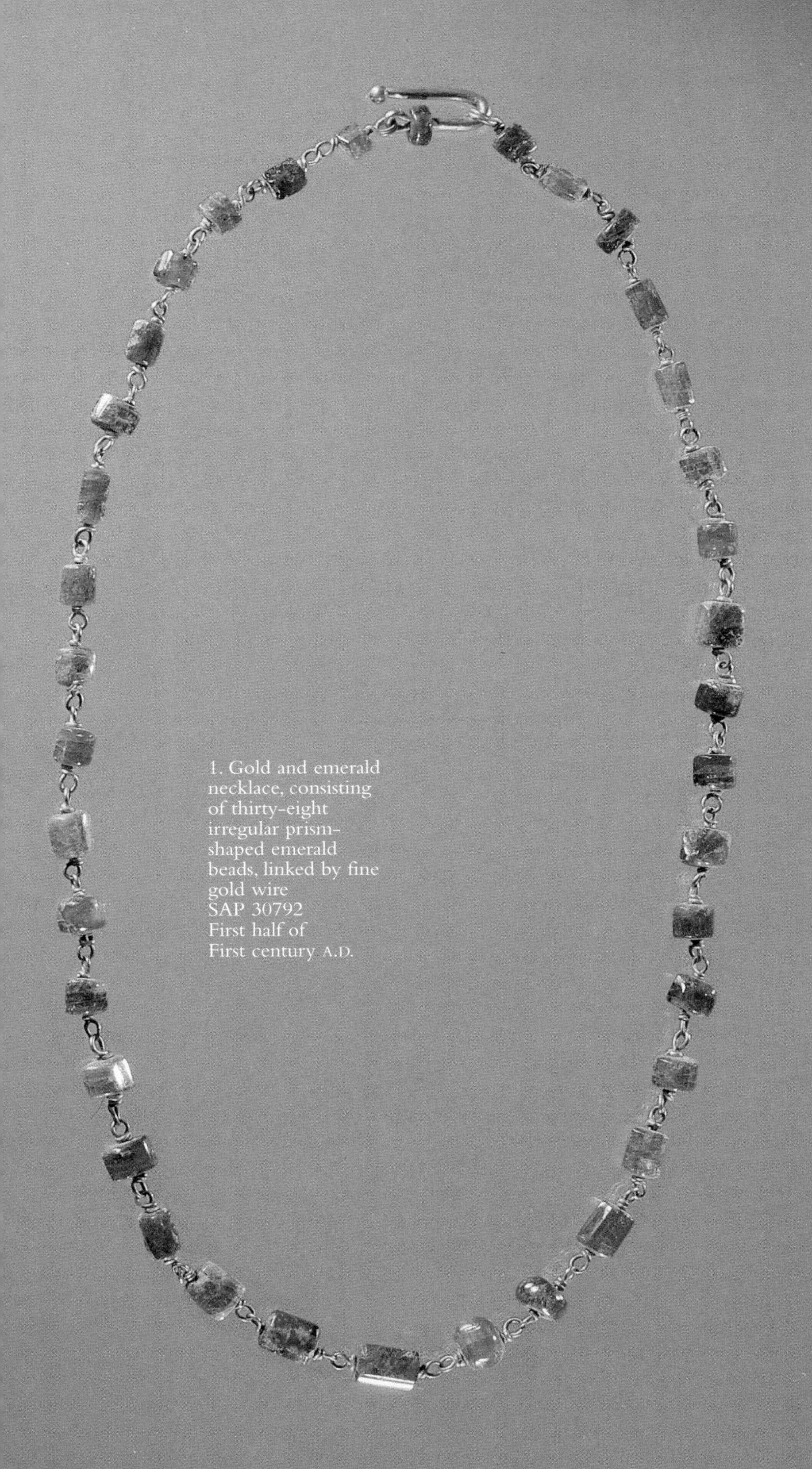

1. Gold and emerald necklace, consisting of thirty-eight irregular prism-shaped emerald beads, linked by fine gold wire
SAP 30792
First half of
First century A.D.

2. Gold necklace of the 'loop-in-loop' type, with central pendant in the shape of a *lunula*
SAP 30793
First half of the first century A.D.

3. Gold necklace made of twenty-two pairs of small lanceolate leaves, probably myrtle, and of seventy-eight little cylinders
SAP 30797
First half of the first century A.D.

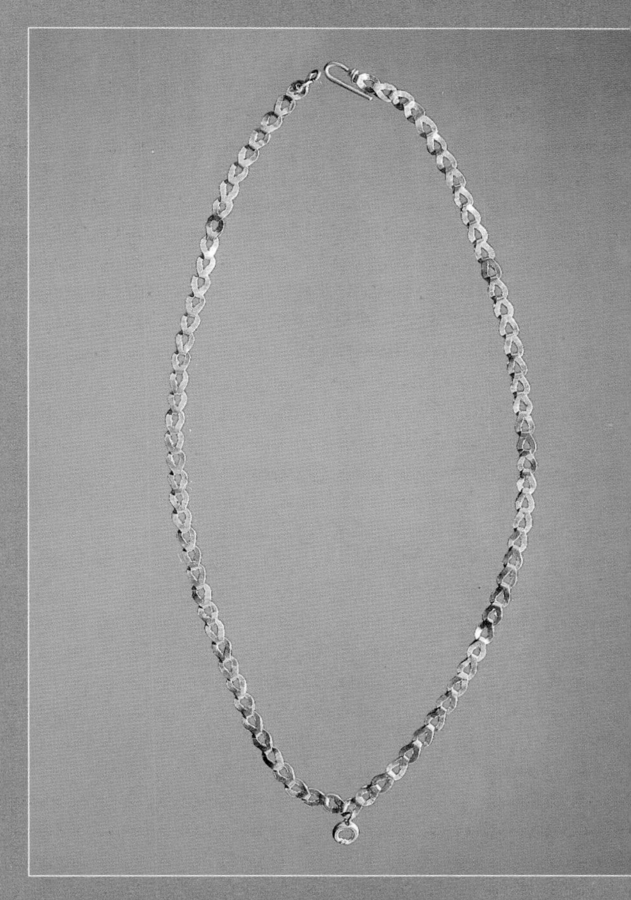

4. Silver mirror, with smooth circular reflective surface and edge curving slightly inwards, joined to the club-shaped handle by a lionskin
SAP 30796
First century A.D.

5. Cylindrical double-sided *skyphos* on a low circular base with two ring-shaped horizontal handles. One side shows three embossed Erotes with a torch; the other bears three more Erotes, either playing the double flute, lifting a torch or playing the *tympanon*
SAP 33474
First half of First century A.D.

ILLA 6

In recent excavations – between 1993 and 2002 – the production area of the villa and some residential rooms have been unearthed. The structures which are visible today are arranged along two axes of about 90 and 40 metres in length, compensating for the disparity in ground level by the construction of a terracing wall. Originating in the Samnite period, the villa has passed through various building phases, the most important of which can be dated to the first half of the first century B.C. when the splendid Second-style wall-paintings in the master's quarters spell out the residential nature of the space. The finest wall decoration belongs without doubt to the triclinium which opens onto a portico along the entire length of a wall: this large painting (figs. 1–3) set in an architectonic framework, with fluted and scaled columns framing the figures against a red background, requires some sort of ritual interpretation.
In the brief period between the earthquake of 62 A.D. and the eruption, the change of owner coincided with the conversion of the villa into a factory for producing wine. In 79 A.D., when the residential part was abandoned, we can see that the production side of the building was in full swing. The existence of a *torcularium* shows that the building was clearly used as a wine-producing business.
And it is likely that among the seven skeletons which were found on the very threshold of this area, we can identify some slaves who died under the collapsing building, while they tried to flee, carrying with them two keys only (fig. 4). [A. C.]

1. Room 16.
Fresco from the west wall. Central panel of the middle section
SAP 85454
First century A.D.

City and Country

The piece of land known as the *ager pompeianus*, which was methodically marked out and cultivated predominantly with vines and olives, extended westwards to the sea, and was bordered to the north with Herculaneum, to the east with Nola and to the south with the river Sarno, a natural border with the territory of Stabia and Nocera.
From the second century B.C., this vast and highly fertile tract of land witnessed the development of numerous settlements, both of a strictly residential character and of a produce-bearing nature. The villas at Terzigno, the Villa Regina at Boscoreale, the Villa of *Lucius Crassius Tertius* at Oplontis, built on terraces which corresponded to the levels of the terrain, were constructed along streets which converged towards the main communication routes of the territory. [A. C.]

2. Room 16.
Fresco from
the middle section
of the east wall
SAP 85455
First century A.D.

3. Room 16.
Fresco from the east wall: detail with the infant Dionysus on a goat and Maenad
SAP 85455
First century A.D.

4. Iron key and small bronze key, with ring clasp and a rectangular axis
SAP 47148–47138
First century A.D.

Anna Civale Pompeii

From one o'clock in the afternoon of 24th August 79 A.D., and for about nineteen hours thereafter, the eruption lashed the city. The continuous and aggravating rain of volcanic materials – which caused injury and victims among those who were outdoors – increased progressively in density, weight and consequent swift impact on the ground, and caused a deposit which mounted up in the open areas and on the flat roofs of the houses, leading to their collapse and soon reaching the upper floors.

Probably by the afternoon, as the eruption and the earth tremors showed no signs of letting up, some of the inhabitants had already taken the decision to flee. They moved with difficulty through the darkness caused by the dense volcanic cloud, their breathing laboured through the continuous rain of pumice and lapilli which blocked their way. Some people from Pompeii sought shelter in the buildings of what is now the site at Moregine or near the harbour of modern-day Bottaro, from which they must have realised it was impossible to escape by sea. Others headed for the countryside near Nocera.

Many of the people who remained in the city were trapped by the heaps of pumice which obstructed the doors and windows and lost their lives through suffocation or in a final attempt at flight. Others were killed by collapsing buildings. Yet others had found shelter in rooms where the pumice had not reached and from which it was still possible to escape. Others fled to upper floors of buildings, where they were blocked in.

Around eight in the evening, after huge deposits of pyroclastic material from the volcano, dumped in the preceding seven hours, had seriously undermined the building structures on which they fell, a sudden new stroke from the volcano belched out a cloud of grey pumice of greater size and density. At sunset, this gave way to a less violent phase of the eruption, marked by a heavy fall of ash and some strong earthquakes during the night.

The let-up in the fall of volcanic material made the surviving Pompeians, who had taken refuge inside the houses, go outside in an attempt at finding a way to escape from the city. They walked with difficulty on the pumice stones, often in little groups, their breathing laboured on account of the ash in the air, helping themselves with lanterns, and they made for the southern part of the city, trying to reach the roads which led away from it.

Dawn was near, but the darkness, caused by the dense ash clouds, continued. At dawn a new surge – the third from the volcano, the first which reached Pompeii – caused the death of those who were outside the city walls, in the Villa of the Mysteries and in the Villa of Diomedes.

From seven-thirty in the morning onwards, the volcano produced the three surges which, in half an hour, buried Pompeii. The first two reached the center of the city, killing those who were wandering through the streets and those who had taken refuge on the upper floors of buildings or in cellars and lower floors. The final surge, at about eight o'clock in the morning, descended on a lifeless city, knocking down the higher walls of the buildings and also dragging with it the bodies of the victims.

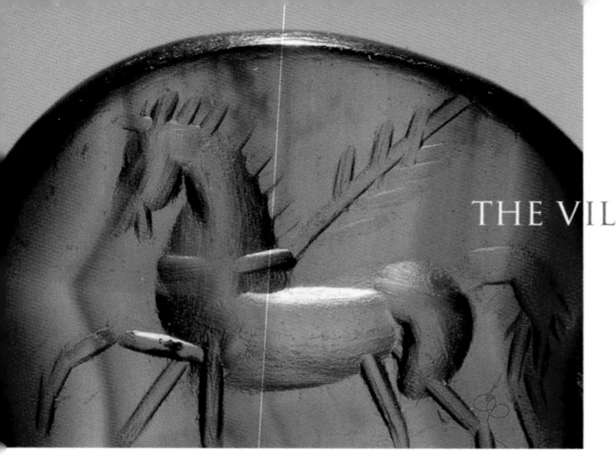

THE VILLA OF DIOMEDES

The excavations of the Villa of Diomedes began in 1771 and continued until 1774 under the direction of Francesco La Vega. The discovery of the building, along the Via dei Sepolcri, outside the Herculaneum Gate, happened almost by chance. When the excavations were completed, it became instantly clear that this was a suburban villa of great importance, which could be regarded as a typical luxury dwelling of the first century A.D. The construction, of the type with descending terraces linked on two levels, goes back to the second century B.C. but was later reduced in size, probably as a consequence of the colonisation of 80 B.C., when the old atrium was partly knocked down to make way for the new road to Herculaneum. The discovery was of great archaeological significance, so much as to make the villa one of the Grand Tour goals, on a par with the tombs of Pompeii. Most Italian and European aristocrats, writers and inquisitive travellers could not get enough of listening to the stories told by the guides at Pompeii, who dwelt on the most macabre details of the tragedy which took place in the villa.
It was the Villa of Diomedes, and the archaeological material it provided, which inspired the long string of learned and romantic books about the dead city, culminating in the Gothic novel which we find in European literature of the nineteenth century. Théophile Gautier's *Arria Marcella* (1852) is set in the villa, as is the action of Ferdinand Gregorovius' Pompeian poem entitled *Euphorion* (1858).
In 1771 two fugitives were found in the portico surrounding the garden, one of whom held an iron key in his hand and wore a gold ring on his finger. Next to him, wrapped in a cloth, were ten gold coins, eighty-eight silver coins and nine bronze ones; a hoard which is among the largest found at Pompeii.
The discovery of these two people immediately became famous in Pompeian literature: the story was put about of a *dominus* and a slave who were trying to escape towards the countryside and the sea, but who were struck down by sudden death near the entrance door to the portico, towards the back wall of the garden. The following year, the find of other skeletons, "eighteen adult skeletons, as well as one of a boy and of a little baby", made the discovery of the villa instantly famous.
In the *cryptoporticus* corridor, near the entrance ramp – where wine amphorae were found, some full some empty – twenty bodies of victims were discovered in the layer of ash on the original floor, piled one on the other; they must have fled there in a vain attempt at escaping from the catastrophe.
The "flood of very liquid material", i.e. ash mixed with water, made its way into the whole room and once hardened, had preserved the imprints and cavities formed by the bodies and other perishable material, forming a kind of mould. Well preserved are above all a box and a heap of little wooden slats, bones inside the imprints

of the bodies, "remains of articles of clothing, sometimes worn one on top of the other", and finally, even hair, attached to some of the skulls, among which it was possible to make out a plaited coiffure. Of the "16 pieces of these corpse-moulds" that were hacked out of the solidified ash to be sent to the museum, it was only possible to save "the breast of a woman covered in a garment" which was taken to the Real Gabinetto at Portici, where the museum and the Villa Reale were located, and subsequently to the Palazzo degli Studi in Naples. This alluring breast, which inspired Théophile Gautier to write his *Arria Marcella,* in its Pompeian setting, also drew the attention of some nineteenth-century scholars of physics and geology. Within a short time, the find became so renowned hat it was submitted to every type of chemical and physical analysis, including the rather aggressive nitric acid test. This was – not surprisingly – probably one of the causes of the destruction of the 'empreinte creuse' which had already occurred by the 1850s. Besides this young woman, another female was found – remarkable for the finely woven texture of her clothes, the richness of her jewels (necklaces, armbands, gold and jewelled rings), and the little hoard of coins found next to her – probably the mistress of the house. Among the imprints which the excavators were able to observe, were also those of people wearing canvas or cloth socks "cut like long trousers; some had no shoes at all". They were probably fourteen servants who were accompanying the two women and two children. The reconstruction of the tragedy which unrolled in the Villa of Diomedes probably runs as follows: the owner, in order to be able to ensure everyone's safety, conducted his family and servants into the *cryptoporticus*, which was lit by skylights giving onto the garden. The family was probably made up of the owner's wife – who was wearing precious necklaces and bracelets – of the son carried in his mother's arms, and of the daughter, adorned with gold jewels. The head of the family probably had bread, fruit and other provisions brought to them while they waited for the fall of pumice to cease. Then, followed by a slave, he went towards the exit with the house key in his hand, and a canvas sack in which he had had the foresight to stash ten gold and eighty-eight silver coins. But they did not get far, since they lost their lives due to the sudden arrival of the *nuée ardente* (pyroclastic surge). The family and servants met the same end, suffocated by the ash which came in through the skylights and asphyxiated them with deadly fumes. The young daughter tried to hide her head in her tunic. Of the objects found near the victims, only a necklace (fig. 1) and gemstone (fig. 2) on display, have been preserved in the National Archaeological Museum in Naples. No trace remains of the other precious objects mentioned in the eighteenth-century excavation reports. [T. R.]

1. Gold chain necklace of the 'loop-in-loop' type, with a small crescent-shaped ring and a boss from which two small chains hang ending in vine-leaves MANN 24833 First century A.D.

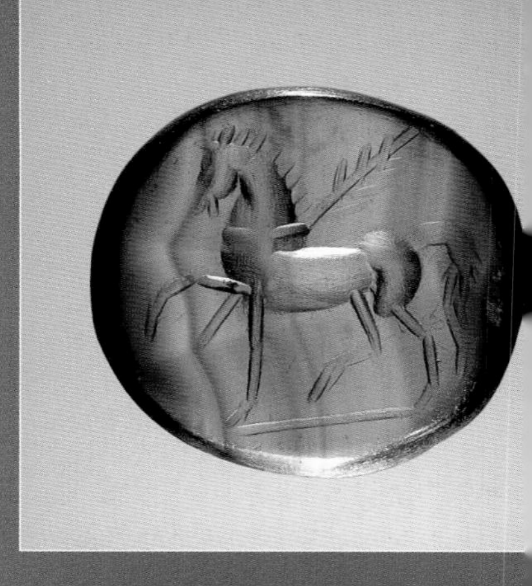

2. Engraved cornelian with profile figure of victorious horse with palm leaf, raising its hoofs SAP 27247 First century A.D.

THE TEMPLE OF ISIS (VIII, 7, 27–28)

The temple, which was hit by the eruption at a fully functional moment, provided its investigators, under the direction of the Bourbon military engineer Francesco La Vega, with almost intact decorations and furnishings (fig. 1).
It was excavated in two years, between 1764 and 1766.
The temple stands in the area of the Triangular Forum, immediately to the north of the theatre.
An inscription on the architrave of the entrance door records how the original structure, that can be dated to the Samnite era and which was entirely destroyed by the earthquake of 62 A.D., was reconstructed by a six-year-old child, Numerius Popidius Celsinus, whose father, the freedman Numerius thought thereby to guarantee his public career. The different spaces within the complex – corresponding to various rites – were closed off by a colonnaded enclosure (fig. 2) whose frescoed walls portrayed processions of priests and priestesses, a mirrored image of the actual parades which took place there.
In the centre of the courtyard is the temple, prostyle tetrastyle on a high podium, inside which the cult images of Isis and Osiris were kept. The main altar, on which the remains of the final sacrifice were found, is to the left of the temple.
Near the altar was the *purgatorium*, a subterranean room which housed the basin for the sacred Nile water necessary to the ceremonies of purification.
Onto the west side of the courtyard the *ekklesiasterion* opened (fig. 3), reserved for the initiate meetings.
Another room was also reached from the portico, south of the previous one – the *sacrarium* – for cult function as well. Here the new converts were tested on their catechism and sacred objects were kept. To the south-east of the courtyard was a two-storey residential building reserved for the priests and for the faithful who were preparing themselves for the rite of initiation.
The victims found in the excavation of the temple – a skeleton in the *ekklesiasterion* and one in the kitchen of the residential complex – were lacking objects which might help assess their identity or role, although the place of discovery suggests that one was maybe a priest and the other his servant. [A. C.]

The Priests and the Cult of Isis

The daily rite in honour of the unhappy goddess – pursued by the god Seth who killed her husband Osiris and forced her to hide with her son Harpocrates in the swamps in the Nile Delta – was divided up into four cult services. During the first one, at dawn, the temple was opened and purified with fire and Nile water. The statue of Isis was washed, dressed and adorned with jewels to be offered to the veneration of the faithful. In the course of the day, for two further times, the goddess and the river water, whose life-giving power was regarded as immanent, were honoured by the singing of hymns. At the end of the day, the statue was undressed, the *cella* doors were shut and the sanctuary was closed for the night.

There were two main festivals during the year. The first, the *Isia*, took place in autumn, from 13th–16th November and re-enacted the death of Osiris, the difficult search by Isis for his dismembered body and, finally, the joy of resurrection. The ritual involved the purification of those faithful to the goddess and the initiation of new members to the cult. The second festival, the *Navigium Isidis*, in March (on the fifth day) – when the sea was once again navigable after the winter storms – honoured the goddess in her role as protectress of sailors. Priests and congregation carried Isis' boat in procession onto the beach and with a prayer launched it on the sea.

The elaborate rituals in honour of the goddess were finely divided up. Next to the main priest, who had acknowledged gifts of divination, came the priests who guarded the sacred fire, the singer, the guardian of the goddess' clothes and jewels, the sacred scribe, the guardian of the keys of the temple and the astrologer as well as numerous semi-priestly acolytes.

The priests led an austere and rigorous life, in which strong emphasis was put on cleanliness of both physical and spiritual nature. The whole body was shaven every three days, and washing in cold water was a strict and frequent duty, day and night. The gleam of white linen clothing and papyrus sandles was part of this very cleanliness. [A. C.]

1. Pair of bronze candelabra, with moulded circular-sectioned stems, quandrangular foot with moulded ionic echinus and angular volutes on the upper part, lion's paws and vertical palmettes on the lower part MANN 72192–72193 First century A.D.

2. *Harpocrates*, fresco from the portico. The statue of the young god is portayed nude, with gold on his head. He holds his right index-finger to his mouth and in his left hand a cornucopia. A priest, carrying two long silver candelabra, approaches from the left MANN 8975 First century A.D.

3. *Io at Canopus.* Fresco from the central section of the south wall of the *ekklesiasterion.* The scene derives from a late-Hellenistic prototype. Io, pursued by Juno, having wandered far and wide in the guise of a cow, arrives in Egypt where she is welcomed by Isis in her sanctuary at Canopus on the Delta. Here she regains her human form and gives birth to Epaphus who founds the Egyptian royal dynasty MANN 9558 First century A.D

THE QUADRIPORTICUS OF THE THEATRES (VIII, 7, 16–17)

The excavation of the Quadriporticus of the Theatres – started between 1766 and 1769, resumed between 1774 and 1779, and completed between 1792 and 1796 – is one of the oldest discoveries made in Pompeii during the Bourbon era. The building, located behind the Large Theatre, is a large quadrangular courtyard surrounded on four sides by a portico of seventy-four doric columns of stuccoed tufa. Built between the second and the beginning of the first century B.C. as a *porticus post scaenam*, or rather a sort of *foyer* to host spectators during the intervals between shows and in the case of rain, it was subsequently transformed into a barracks for housing and training gladiators (*ludus*), after the earthquake of 62 A.D. had put the *Regio* V Gladiators' Barracks out of use.
It was probably in this final phase that a series of small rooms was added on two floors around the central exercise area: gladiators' cells, a kitchen and refectory as well as service rooms. The rooms on the upper floor probably housed the *lanista*, the gladiators' trainer and manager.
The discovery of a considerable number of bronze gladiatorial parade weapons, many decorated with mythological scenes, has been a key factor in the identification of the use of this building. Fifteen helmets (figs. 1, 2) have been found, along with fourteen shin-guards (fig. 3) six shoulder-guards, three sword-belts, two daggers, a sword and lance tips.
When the building was first excavated, a great number of skeletons was found both in the rooms and outside, some of them of particular interest.
The earliest find, consisting of four adult skeletons in a room on the west side, near a beam with shackles for ten people – though they were not found attached to it – has suggested that the room was a slave prison, which would be very likely in a gladiators' barracks.
Another skeleton found under the stairs, near two cups, a silver disc, and the skeleton of a horse, can possibly be identified as a type of gladiator who fought from horseback: the *eques*. Besides thirty-four skeletons, remarkable for their number but not for any object found with them, there was a particularly interesting discovery in one room of the Quadriporticus where gladiatorial weapons and three wooden boxes were found – one of which containing the remains of fabric quilted with gold thread, probably parade uniforms – along with a skeleton, perhaps that of a woman, wearing a rich *parure* of jewellery (rings with gemstones [figs. 4, 5], earrings, armbands and a valuable necklace with twelve emeralds). From this find arose the story, now legendary in Pompeian literature, of the rich matron who was caught short by the eruption of Vesuvius while she was visiting her gladiator-lover.
In any case, without completely discounting this hypothesis, one must point out that the rich lady was not alone in the room. At least eighteen other skeletons were found after hers, some of them perhaps children, considering the small dimension of the room.
Therefore, it is more likely to identify this as a group of Pompeians who, in attempting to flee to the countryside or the sea, had looked for a building to shelter from the fall of volcanic material.
If this were the case, the rich lady could have arrived in the Gladiators' Barracks merely by chance, and perhaps was the last person to join the group of fugitives, as she was found near the entrance. [T. R.]

Gladiators and Games at Pompeii

Gladiatorial games were usually organised in such a way as to put together in the arena pairs (*paria*) of different kinds of fighters, distinguishable by their armour. At Pompeii, the large numbers of playbills found on the walls of many buildings show various different numbers of these pairs of gladiators, ranging from ten to forty-nine pairs, but the average was probably about twenty.

The typical day at the gladiatorial games was fixed definitively in the Augustan period. The morning started with beast fights (*venatio*) and the execution of condemned prisoners (*damnatio ad bestias*), followed by entertainments in the lunch interval and gladiatorial games (*munera*) in the afternoon. The public participated with great enthusiasm and some famous gladiators had a considerable fan following. Moreover, from what we can gather from some Pompeian graffiti, quite apart from their general popularity, gladiators also were the heartthrobs of their female fans.

It was during a show of gladiatorial games in 59 A.D. that a bloody brawl broke out in the Amphitheatre at Pompeii between the citizens of Pompeii and those of Nocera, so violent as to be even recorded in Tacitus' *Annals* (XIV, 17). A well-known Pompeian fresco, preserved in the Archaeological Museum in Naples has left an almost photographic record of this bit of local drama. The Roman Senate, called to intervene, had no choice but to impose sanctions upon Pompeii: gladiatorial shows were suspended for ten years, illegally-formed clubs were banned and those who had organised these ill-fated games were banished. [T. R.]

1. Bronze gladiator's helmet with hemispherical crown, and visor on the upper part
MANN 5674
First century A.D.

2. Gladiator's bronze helmet: the relief shows in the centre a personification of Rome, bearing weapons, and on the sides, kneeling barbarians, prisoners and trophies
MANN 5674
First century A.D.

3. Gladiator's bronze shin-guard (*ocrea*): the relief decoration depicts Athena, armed with a lance and a shield, towards whom two cupids fly carrying her helmet and *ocrea*
MANN 5664
First century A.D.

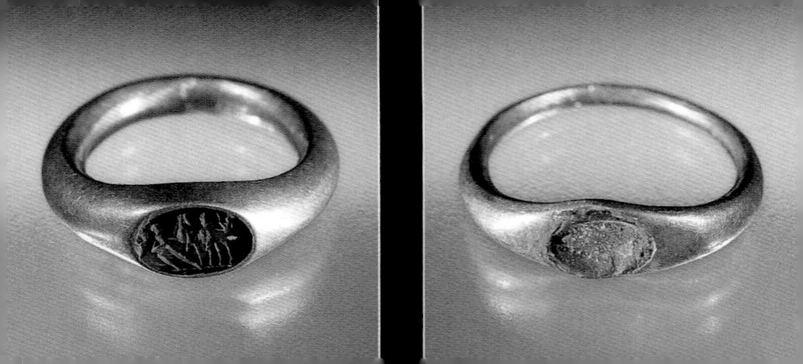

[VIC]OLO DEGLI SCHELETRI

The Alley of the Skeletons (Vicolo degli Scheletri), parallel to the first stretch of the Via dell'Abbondanza, owes its name to the discovery, in February 1863, of the skeletons of four people, and to the use, here for the first time, of casting them in plaster, something which had previously only been done for wooden furniture.
The group consists of a man and three women – perhaps a whole family who died at dawn on 25th August while attempting to escape from the city.
The old *pater familias* led the group carrying the family's most valuable goods: their savings, some gold jewellery and the house keys.
The violence of the surge threw him to the ground: he tried, without success, to get up again, leaning on his elbow and protecting his head with an edge of his cloak.
He was followed, a few steps behind, by his two daughters who fell together. The younger of the two had her hair in a plait; neither of them wore any jewellery. Their mother, lifting her skirts as she ran, was the last of the group; she wore a few jewels and carried with her some other precious objects in a bag, among which an amber statuette (fig. 1) and the family silver: a few pieces of tableware (fig. 2) and some mirrors from the *argentum balneare* (fig. 3).
[A. C.]

1. Amber statuette depicting a chubby boy (a cupid?), his face framed by a head of curls and his body entirely wrapped in a large cloak. He holds an (unidentifiable) object on his right shoulder
MANN 25813
First century A.D.

2. Silver medallion, perhaps the *emblema* of a goblet or a plate, with an image of Fortune in the centre, standing and holding a *patera* in her extended right hand and a cornucopia in the left
MANN 25489
First century B.C.–first century A.D.

3. Silver mirror, its border decorated with a series of incised palmettes. The moulded handle is attached to the circular section by two stylised bird heads
MANN 25716
First century B.C.–first century A.D.

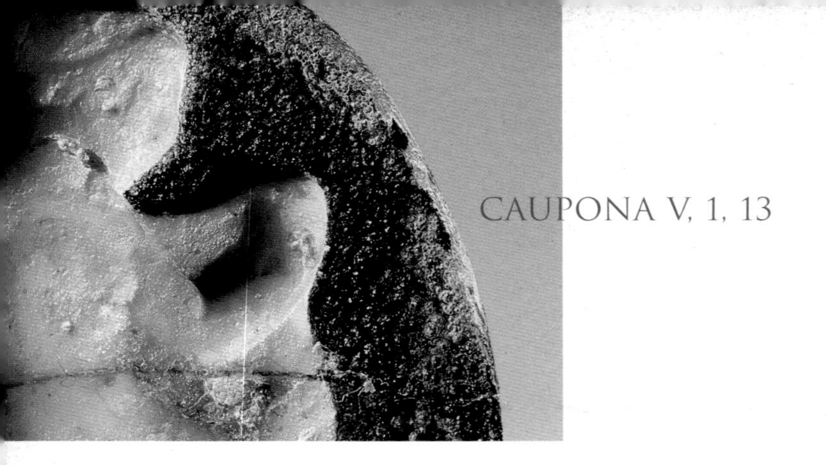

CAUPONA V, 1, 13

Also known as the Inn of *Salvius*, this large complex occupying almost all the northern sector of its *insula*, was completely excavated in 1875. A large entrance hall opened onto the selling area, where there was a U-shaped brick counter with six *dolia* set into it, containing the food which was probably also displayed on shelves lining a wall. Two other rooms for customer use were accessible from the shop area, decorated with Fourth-style paintings, and faced onto a courtyard at the end of which was the kitchen. The owner's quarters were on the upper floor.

The body of a fugitive was found in the shop, surrounded by some coins and a remarkable amount of jewellery: five pairs of earrings, eleven gold rings (fig. 1), three silver rings, as well as a spoon and a small silver disc with a head in bas-relief; numerous gemstones (fig. 3) and two bronze signet-rings (figs. 4, 5). The quantity, value and variety of the objects are inconsistent with the modest nature of the shop: it is probable that the Pompeian who died here at dawn on 25th August had dallied behind in his flight to loot whatever he found on his way. [A. C]

1. Gold snake-shaped ring, with double-stranded band, and intertwined head and tail of a snake
MANN 110804
First century A.D.

2. Glass-paste cameo with nude female figure (Aphrodite?) seated in right-hand profile while holding the hem of her cloak in her left hand
MANN 110827
First century A.D.

3. Engraved *prasium* with Nike on a moving chariot, in left-hand profile, with whip in her right hand and reins in the left
MANN 110823
First century A.D.

4, 5. Bronze rings with relief seal print on rectangular block, used for sealing documents and bonds
MANN
110828–110829
First century A.D.

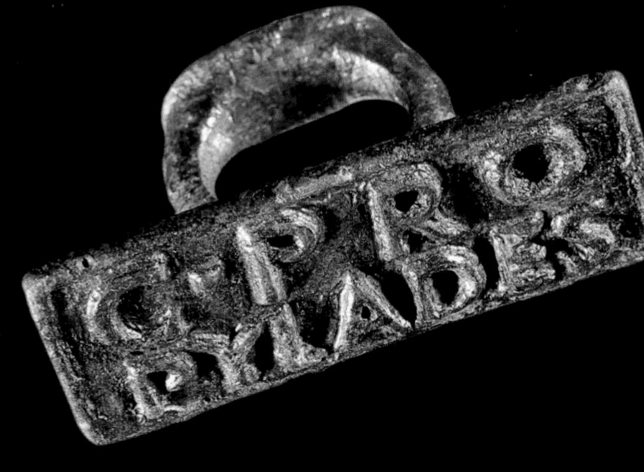

Inns in Pompeii

There were many inns in Pompeii, large and small, both with and without backrooms for the production and sale of food, either to take away or to eat on the premises. The typical structure comprised a counter with one of its short ends joined to the inn wall. Wares were set out on the marble counter-top, or could be ladled out of the huge terra-cotta *dolia* set into it, which generally contained wine, oil and *garum*. Where wine was sold there was almost always a little stove near the counter, used in winter to heat water to dilute the wine. [A. C.]

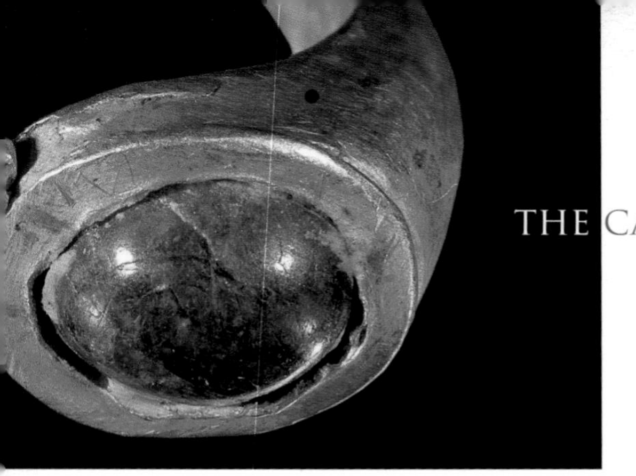

THE CAUPONA OF SALVIUS (VI, 14, 35–36)

This *caupona* (inn) takes its name from an election inscription on one of the walls near the entrance, in which a certain *Salvius* asks someone called *Casellium* to be elected as aedile.
This was a respectable commercial enterprise used for the sale of hot drinks. We can identify its use by the large counter at the corner, with two *dolia* set into it – for which the drinks were heated in a lead cauldron placed on the hearth – the kitchen and the hearth.
There must also have been a small *lararium*, as attested by the discovery of a bronze statuette of Jupiter with thunderbolt and silver sceptre.
At the back, a passage opened onto a room designed for customers who evidently wanted to spend more time in the inn; a wooden staircase at the side of the kitchen led to an upper floor. The mundaine quality of the fresco (fig. 1) decorating the north side of the inn gives an indication of its clientele.
It is divided into four different scenes, each one illustrated by painted inscriptions: a woman (the prostitute *Myrtale*) and a man kissing; a woman serving a large jug and cup, while two customers compete to be served first; a quarrel and brawl between two dice players who are eventually asked to leave the *caupona* by the proprietor.
At the moment of the eruption two people were trying to shelter from the rain of pumice on the upper floor of the building, maybe the owners or the managers of the inn, and in their flight they had taken their most precious valuables: three hundred and five silver coins, six gold coins, and various pieces of gold jewellery – two bracelets (fig. 2), a necklace, two pairs of earrings, eight gold rings (fig. 3) and a single silver one – as well as a silver saucepan.
The 1876 excavation data do not allow us to attribute these objects to people with any certainty: if the gold jewellery and the little hoard of coins belonged to only one person – obviously a woman – she probably came from a family of means.
In any case, at least three of the eight rings seem to have belonged to a child or a young woman. [T. R.]

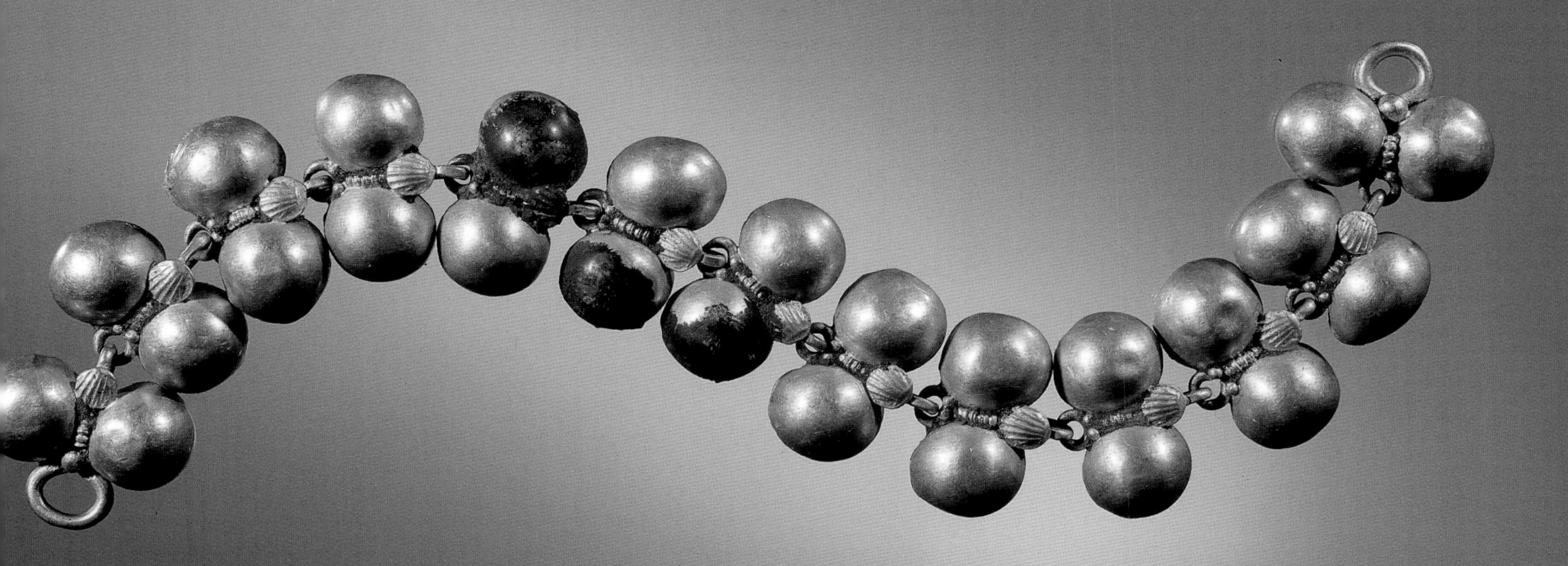

1. Fresco from the north wall of the inn with scenes of a hostelry MANN 111482

2. Gold bracelet with pairs of gold-foil hemispheres, soldered in the middle and held together by knurled wire covered with sea-shell decoration MANN 110919–110920 First century A.D.

3. Gold ring with thick band, ending with a double bezelcontaining green plasma stones MANN 110908 First century A.D.

VICOLO DI TESMUS

The Alley of Thesmus (Vicolo di Tesmo) formed the eastern limit of *Insula* 4 of *Regio* IX, whose whole area had been intended for a bath complex that was never finished, which would have been situated on the intersection of the Via di Nola and the Via Stabiana.
In 1877, the bodies of four fugitives were found on a layer of pumice about 3 metres deep. Even though they were only a few metres from each other, it is impossible to establish whether they were leaving the city together and if the lamp which was found nearby was helping them to light their way. Of these four people perhaps one of them, as indicated by the presence of jewellery, was a woman who was trying to save her *parure* by taking it with her as she fled. Along with a pair of earrings, she had a gold chain necklace with emerald prisms and a long necklace of the 'loop-in-loop' type, with ivy leaves of gold foil (fig. 1) which – in terms of manufacture and design – is one of the most beautiful pieces of jewellery found in the Vesuvius region.
The woman was also carrying two lapis lazuli, as yet uncut, and the family silver which, even if not complete in all its pieces, included both the *argentum potorium* (fig. 2) and *escarium* (fig. 3), as well as the *argentum balneare*. [A. C.]

1. *Catena* made up of ninety-four ivy leaves of gold foil, joined by small rings – partly covered with little bosses – and fastened with two smooth circular bosses
MANN
111113–111114
First century A.D.

2. Shell-shaped silver vessels on three round feet. Slightly different in dimensions, to allow for stacking, they were used for washing or pouring liquids
MANN
111121–111122
First century A.D.

3. Silver spoons, used either for eating eggs and shellfish, or for cosmetics
MANN
111135–111136–111137
First century A.D.

THE HOUSE OF OPPIUS GRATUS (IX, 6, 5)

Excavated between October and December 1878, this rather modest *domus* originates from the unification of two different houses. The use of limestone from the Sarno dates its construction to the first half of the second century B.C., but there were many subsequent re-buildings and work was still in progress at the time of the eruption, as witnessed by the accounts relating to the materials used and the workmen's days, written in charcoal on the walls of the atrium and kitchen.
An inscription in white tesserae on the atrium floor, now lost, recorded the name of the mosaic-artist (*musivarius*) who had made it and that of the owners: *Quartilla* and the architect *Gratus*, whose profession has been inferred by the find within the house of a *circinus* (compass) and an inkpot (fig. 1).
The discovery of a large amount of kitchenware and tableware – both in terra-cotta and in metal – of lamps, tools and marble furnishings under the colonnades of the peristyle, suggests that these heterogeneous items had been put in a storeroom by the owners, and had been vainly moved into the portico in the hope of being able to save them.
Near the door of the triclinium the body of a fugitive was found: he had with him fifty-nine silver coins, a gold ring, a silver one, and nine bronze bracelets (fig. 2), as well as some mirrors and three statuettes – two of the Lares (fig. 3) and a bronze one of Mercury (fig. 4).
Not much else can be said about this person, who was certainly trying to escape through the *tablinum*: was he the owner of the house, a steward supervising the building works or a thief taking the few remaining valuable objects in the house as he fled?
[A. C.]

1. Octagonal bronze inkpot with ring-clasp and hinged lid, its body made up of soldered metal sections and its concave top decorated with concentric circles in relief
MANN 115614
First century A.D.

2. Bronze bracelets with hemispheres on flat discs and large eliptical bezel set with a big greenish convex glass paste stone as its fastening. Traces of gilding on the fastening lead one to suspect that the bracelets must have looked more precious than they actually were
MANN 118270-118271
First century A.D.

3. Bronze statuettes of Lares. The house and family divinities are represented in mirror image, in dancing step, holding up the drinking horn (*rython*) in one hand and the *patera* in the other
MANN 115555–115556
First century A.D.

4. Bronze statuette of Mercury. The god is running forward – his petasus on his head and his cloak flying behind him – while holding a bag in his right hand and the caduceus in his left
MANN 115554
First century A.D.

HOUSE OF THE CENTENARY (IX, 8, 3–5)

This sumptuous house dating from the Samnite period, with a double Tuscan atrium and an almost square peristyle, was discovered in the year of the eighteenth centenary of the eruption, between May 1879 and September 1880.
One of the largest *domus* of Pompeii (about 1800 square metres), it is the result of the addition of at least three different houses, something which explains the complexity of its layout, as well as the fine decorative quality of some of its rooms (fig. 1), as opposed to others which are crudely painted.
The history of the construction phases of the *domus* and the *insula* in which it stands is long and complicated. From the second century B.C. until 79 A.D. renovations were almost continuous. Changes were made not only to the decoration but also to the entrances (fig. 2), the inner corridors, as well as to the use and hierarchy of the rooms.
In the final phase, before the eruption, the *dominus*, who was probably a rich *vinarius* of freedman extraction, brought about substantial conversions to the organisation and function of the rooms: the main atrium was turned into a space to be used for the production and marketing of wine, while the rooms which opened off it were equipped with sturdy wooden racks for storing the wine. The identification of the owner as a *vinarius* is also owed to the presence, decorating the *lararium* in the second atrium, of a picture of Bacchus (fig. 3).

The house has yielded the skeletons of three victims.
The first two were found in a room immediately to the east of the smaller atrium; according to the excavation reports which recorded the find at the time, no objects were found with them.
The third skeleton was discovered in a connecting corridor between the peristyle and the private apartment decorated with erotic scenes.
In conjuction with this, the presence of jewels – an armband in the shape of a snake, a gold earring with a pearl, a silver hairpin – would indicate that the skeleton was that of a woman. Next to it a spoon, two door keys and a hoard of thirty-eight coins were also found. [A. C.]

1. Mosaic *emblema* with a polychrome *Gorgoneion*, framed by two small landscape scenes in black and white. It decorated the centre of the floor of bedroom 12
MANN 112284
End of first century B.C.–beginning of first century A.D.

2. Bronze statuette of Satyr with wineskin once decorating the peristyle of the house, where it was used as a fountainhead
MANN 111495
First century A.D.

3. Fresco of Bacchus. The god, leaning on a *thyrsus* and with a *kantharos* in his right hand, is clad in a bunch of grapes at the foot of a high mountain covered with vineyards, which some scholars identify as Mount Vesuvius
MANN 112286
First century A.D., Fourth Style.

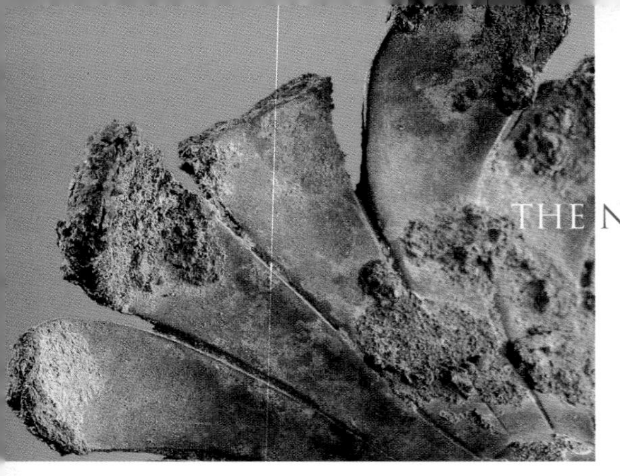

THE NOLAN GATE

This complex structure (square base, barrel vault and two towers flanking its front inside the city walls) whose construction can be dated at about 300 B.C., is situated at the furthest eastern point of the *decumanus maximus* which crossed Pompeii in a west-east direction.
Its location at the end of one of the main roads of the city made it one of the better escape routes for those who chose to flee to the countryside around Nocera and the Sarno river. Indeed, over a long period of time, and in subsequent stages – from 1854 to 1976 – excavations outside the gate have revealed a good thirty-three bodies, who fell among the tombs on either side of the street. Twelve of the fugitives tried to get away from the city hit by the lapilli, but were submerged by the incandescent rain. The rest tried to make their way on the pumice at dawn on 25th August, taking advantage of the respite during the eruption, but they were knocked down and suffocated by the surges. A couple of people were trying to lighten their way with a lamp (fig. 1), carrying only their house key. Many people fled alone, with a few coins enclosed in little cloth bags.
The women carried with them their own possessions: one of them, who fell near the tomb of *Aesquillia Polla*, was clutching a canvas bag which contained, as well as keys and a little hoard of coins, a cylindrical box and a silver statuette base. Another woman, a bit further on, was carrying her jewels, stashed in a wooden box, in order to preserve them better (fig. 2).
Fifteen victims were found together in a narrow space – almost all men – knocked down by the surge which dragged detritus and uprooted trees at the speed of the *nuée ardente*. Only one man was carrying a dagger (fig. 3) and a large knife (fig. 4), while near one of the few women in the group, a little hoard of silver and bronze coins was found. This very young girl was wearing her jewels and carrying a statuette of Isis Fortuna (fig. 5), in the hope that the goddess would protect her during her flight.
[A. C.]

1. Single-wick bronze oil-lamp, in the shape of a head with negro features. The eye cavities contained different coloured materials to represent his pupils
MANN 133320
First century A.D.

2. Gold *catena*, with chain of the 'loop-in-loop' type, and pendant made of *lunula* with joining horns, decorated with four little spheres
SAP 866
First century A.D.

3. Wooden dagger sheath (restored), decorated with a band at the base and a bronze point at the tip ending with a shell-shaped knob
SAP 17048
First century A.D.

4. Large knife in a sheath made from wood, silver-plated bronze and iron. The iron blade is inserted into a wooden sheath with silver-plated bronze appliqué decoration consisting of incised geometric motifs: two small rings at the side were used to buckle it on
SAP 17047
First century A.D.

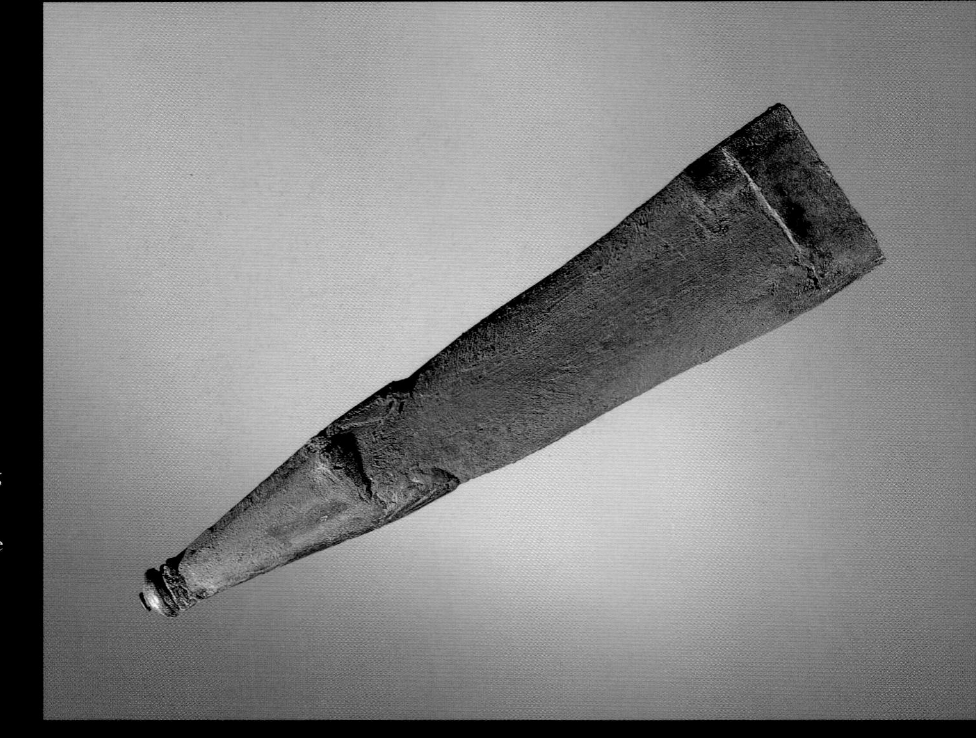

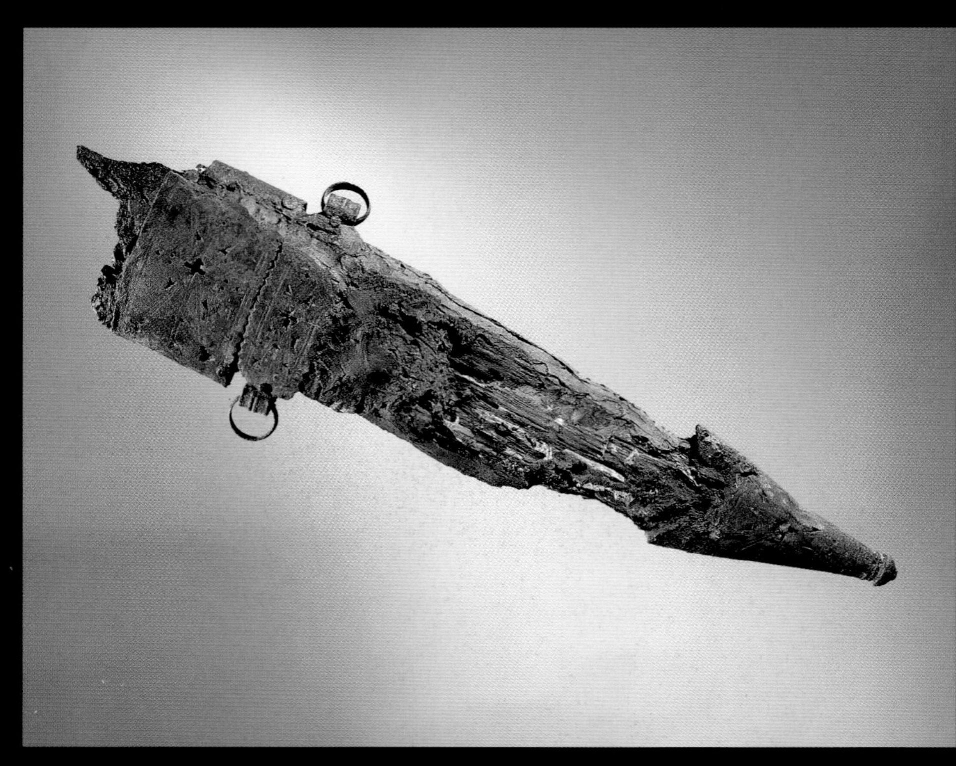

5. Silver statuette
of Isis Fortuna.
The goddess,
on a throne,
is wearing a chiton
and a himation.
In her right hand
she holds a rudder,
in her left
a cornucopia which
leans against her
shoulder
SAP 15496
First century A.D.

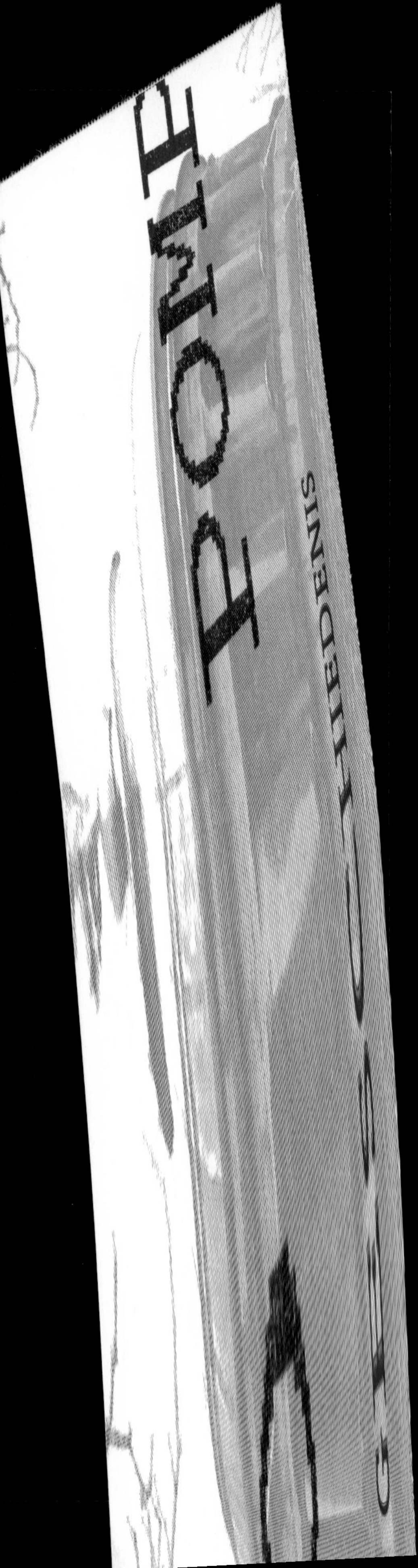

THE VESUVIUS GATE

The gate, which formed the northernmost limit of the Via Stabiana, the main south-east/north-west axis of the city, was excavated in 1902. From there – the highest part of the city nearest to the slopes of the volcano – a road departed, skirting the city walls, crossing a necropolis area and then heading towards the northern suburbs.
It is likely that the two fugitives who were found near the gate, next to the monumental tombs of the necropolis, came from this area and its villas.
The first was carrying a few coins (fig. 1) and some rings; the second, killed by the surge which hit Pompeii in the early hours of 25th August, was trying to escape along the city walls with a more substantial hoard of coins, some pieces of *argentum escarium* (fig. 2), a few inexpensive jewels, two keys and a hemp rope, which perhaps he thought might prove useful during the escape. [A. C.]

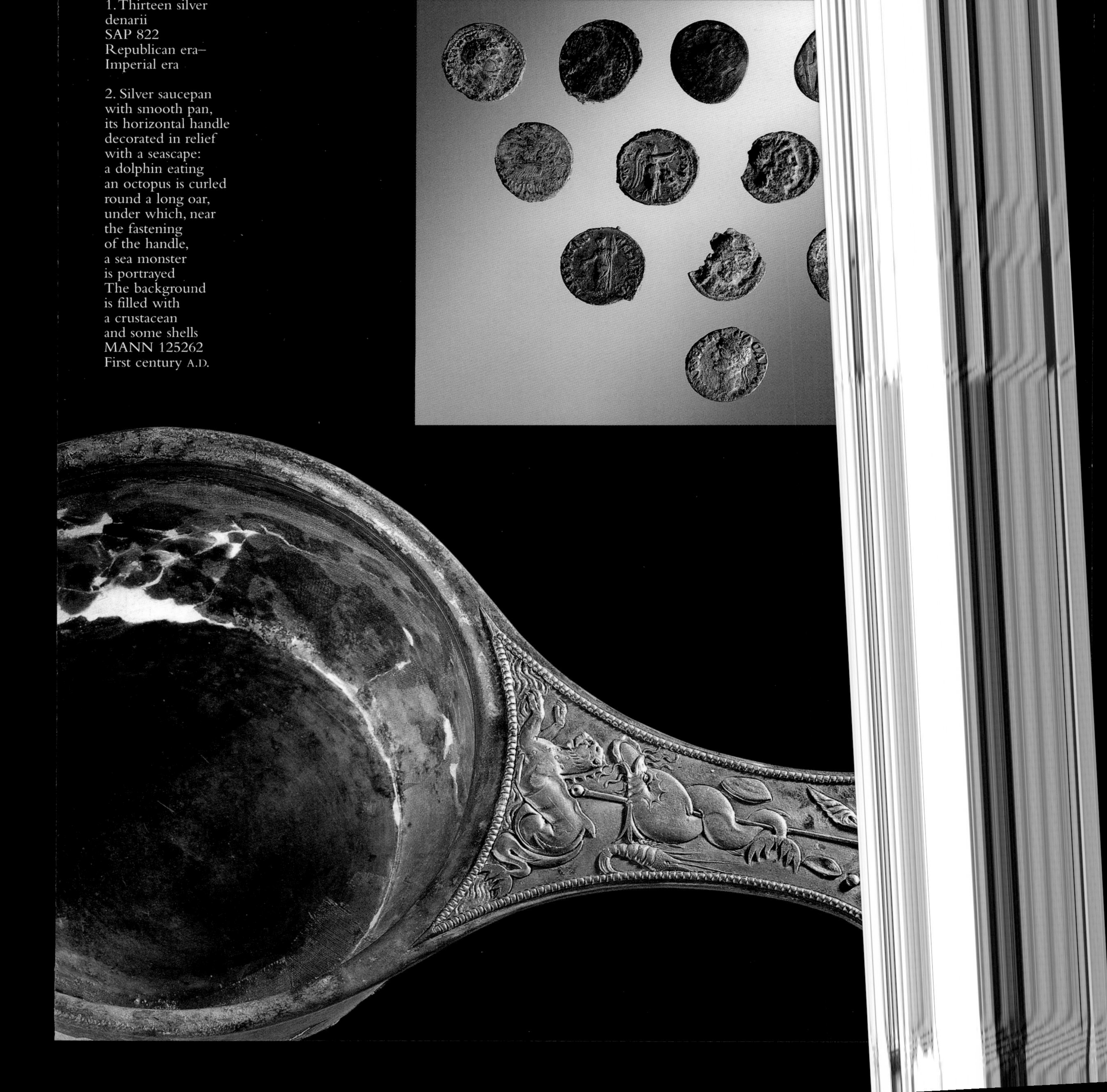

1. Thirteen silver denarii
SAP 822
Republican era–Imperial era

2. Silver saucepan with smooth pan, its horizontal handle decorated in relief with a seascape: a dolphin eating an octopus is curled round a long oar, under which, near the fastening of the handle, a sea monster is portrayed The background is filled with a crustacean and some shells
MANN 125262
First century A.D.

THE HOUSE OF THE CRYPTOPORTICUS (I, 6, 2)

The House of the Cryptoporticus, located near the Via dell'Abbondanza, was in the process of being restructured at the time of the eruption to shore up the damage caused by the frequent earth tremors which had occurred between 62 and 79 A.D.
Originally, the house was joined to the neighbouring House of the Trojan Shrine, and was one large establishment with two atria, a garden and colonnades, but after the earthquake of 62 A.D. it was divided off from it.
In the course of this renovation, the *cryptoporticus* – from which the house takes its name – as well as the terrace above it, containing at that time a large brick triclinium (dining room) for summer banquets, were cut off from the House of the Trojan Shrine and joined to the smaller house as a cellar.
The galleries of the *cryptoporticus* were filled in with building rubble and shut off with walls: only one wing was spared (and made accessible by a new staircase) to be used as a wine-cellar and storeroom for the summer dining room above, shaded by a pergola and installed in the old loggia, probably open to the public. The use of the room as a cellar meant that it was not redecorated and its splendid paintings, associated with its previous function, were preserved.
The pictures and stuccoes, which make up one of the most impressive examples of the final phase of Second Style (40–30 B.C.) were already 100 years old when the disaster struck.
The original wall-painting is also preserved in another room, the *oecus* – on show in the exhibition – similar in both composition and high quality to that of the *cryptoporticus* (figs. 1, 2).
The elegant pictorial scheme is rhythmised by herms on pedestals supporting, against a background of garlands and festoons, the planks of a coffered ceiling: on the frieze of the metopes are little pictures (*pinakes*) framed by folding wooden shutters, depicting still-life paintings and symbolic scenes relating to the Dionysiac mysteries.
On the only surviving fragment of the decoration of the north wall of the room is a *pinax* with the scene of Ariadne carried on a chariot, perhaps for her marriage, led by a female figure playing the double flute.
In 1914, a group of victims was found in the garden of the House of the Cryptoporticus, perhaps residents of the building or customers

of the summer triclinium which had been opened to the public. At dawn on 25th August, perhaps taking advantage of the diminishing fall of pumice, they may have decided to abandon the *cryptoporticus*, where they had been seeking refuge until then, and climb out of the wide windows, since it was impossible to escape through the room or the side entrance because of the heap of volcanic material.
As they tried to flee towards the outer wall of the building to reach the nearby street, some people – one of whom was wearing a gold ring with a gemstone (fig. 3) – crossed the garden above, protecting their heads with tiles. Unfortunately, the arrival of the *nuée ardente* (surges 4 and 5) must have nullified their attempt and they collapsed while trying to cover their heads, suffocated by the fall of ash. This escaping method brings to mind Pliny's account of Pomponianus and his retinue who, having spent the night in the villa at Stabia, tried to escape protecting their heads with cushions against the falling pumice.
Among the victims of the House of the Cryptoporticus, of whom casts have been made, we find two bodies embracing each other – perhaps a mother and a daughter – an adolescent of about fifteen years old – whose shoes (*crepida*) are still identifiable, with nailed-on soles, open heels and laces – and a crouching man trying to free his ankles from two large iron rings (*compedes*). This man, who was wearing a bronze armband with snake heads, can surely be identified as a slave because of the presence of the *compedes*, making him to date the third case
on his ankles
The other pe
to belong to
class, judging
with them.
Of the others
is notable; as h
with him two
(*skyphoi*), deco
and a *simpulum*
had obviously
hands.
Here we have
of the discover
the bodies of t
that these kind
not very comm
the exception
silverware disc
such as the Ho
the House of t
and House VII

1, 2. Details
of the fresco from
the north and south
walls of the *oecus*
of the house
SAP 59468
40-20 B.C., Second
Style

3. Gold ring with
bezel set with
an engraved garnet
picturing a strutting
cock
MANN 137871
First century A.D.

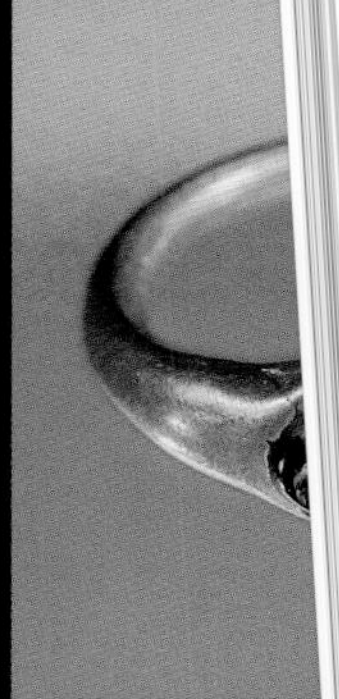

VIA DELL'ABBONDANZA

The lower *decumanus*, the street which crossed the city from east to west, takes its name from a female face – erroneously identified as that of the personification of Abundance – carved into a small pillar above the basin of a public fountain near the Forum.
Many of the finest houses of the city lined this street, together with *cauponae, officinae* and shops for the production and sale of varied goods. The pavements were cluttered with signs, benches, awnings and canopies, to set out and protect the merchandise on sale, and the atmosphere of a big open-air market was reinforced by the presence of numerous wandering street sellers, who mingled with the crowd, in search of customers.
When, on the afternoon of 24th August, pumice and fragments of burning hot stone started to fall on the city, the street was quickly filled up and the roofs of the buildings facing onto it, pressed down with the weight of volcanic material, began to collapse, overwhelming those who were trying to get out of the city. Among them were a group of three people who were walking with difficulty on the layer of pumice and a man who, all alone, was trying to light his way with a bronze lantern (fig. 1) in the thick darkness caused by the billowing ash from the slopes of the volcano.
The level of the pumice, which continued to fall without respite, soon reached the height of over 3 metres, trapping the people who had taken temporary refuge in the rooms which looked onto the street. Towards dawn, the eruption lost some of its intensity and the brief calm allowed a girl, who had been driven upstairs by the pumice stones which had flooded into the ground floor of the shop of *Tedia Seconda* (I, 13, 4–5), to lower herself from the balcony in order to find an escape route towards the east. However, in a few moments, the surge caught up with her, overwhelming her and knocking out of her hand the little box with the *parure* of jewels which she was carrying (fig. 2).
The same surge suffocated a man outside the House of *Paquius Proculus*, who had managed to open a hole for himself in the wall to get out of the ground floor of the house, which was by now completely filled with pumice. [A. C.]

1. Bronze lantern with cylindrical body, base in the form of a flat circular surface on two feet, and hemispherical movable lid. The sides, which are not preserved, were made of parchment or animal bladders
SAP 5798
First century A.D.

THE HOUSE OF TREBIUS VALENS (III, 2, 1)

The house, situated on the Via dell'Abbondanza, probably belonged to *Trebius Valens*, a Pompeian citizen who was standing for election as both aedile and *duovir*, as well as supporting other political candidates himself. His name appeared as many as twelve times in numerous electoral slogans and in graffiti on both the inner and the outer walls of the building: unfortunately the inscriptions are no longer visible, because of the bombing of its broad windowless façade with old dado capitals in 1943.
The presence of a graffiti, in one wing of the peristyle, quoting the first line of the *Aeneid* suggests a literary background, or literary contacts on the part of the owner. The *domus*, laid out according to the typical Pompeian plan (atrium, *tablinum*, peristyle and garden) though not large, was decorated with good quality wall-paintings of the Second and Third Style, had decorative garden sculpture and a small bath suite (*balneum*).
The latter, something found only in noble houses, comprised two little rooms decorated with Second-style paintings: the first served the double function of dressing-room and *tepidarium*, the second that of *calidarium*. Valuable objects have been found in some of the cubicles of the house, such as a silver *simpulum* (fig. 1) and three bronze statuettes of Hercules, Venus (fig. 2) and Mercury.
In 1915, during the excavation of the peristyle, the skulls of four victims who doubtless died before they could reach safety, were found in the layer of lapilli. The position of these four Pompeians suggests that they were trying to shelter from the rain of lapilli and debris which was beginning to fill the garden and the portico, by walking along the wall of the ambulatory in an attempt at reaching the eastern passage which could lead them to the atrium, and from there to the street. But when they reached the south-east corner of the peristyle, an unexpected event must have caused their death: the roof of the portico, unable to resist the weight of the volcanic material (pumice) which was gradually increasing as more slipped down from the higher roof behind, collapsed, causing the death of the fugitives, who were struck to the ground or doubled up, as shown by the roof tiles found under their remains.
Wearing pearl earrings and two gold rings, a woman was sitting with her face turned towards the wall, whilst a man, in a crouching position and hands on his chest, was discovered wearing an iron ring with a gemstone on his finger.
Two others were in the same position, one of whom – identified as an adolescent – was carrying a key and a coin with him.
The fugitives did not then have time to gather their own property, but in any case the few ornamental objects belong to a medium to low socio-economic group, clearly lower than that which one would expect from the house.
Bearing this in mind, at the time of the excavation it was suggested that these people, although living in the house, were not its proprietors: more likely they belonged to the owner's family or were some of his slaves. [T. R.]

1. This small silver ladle (*simpulum*), found along with a spoon in a case, was probably part of a dining set
SAP 2173
First century A.D.

2. Bronze nude statuette of Venus with a long lock of hair in her hand
SAP 2275
First century A.D.

THE VILLA OF THE MYSTERIES

Located about 400 metres from the Herculaneum Gate, on the ancient Via *Superior* that linked Pompeii to the suburbs of Oplontis and thence to Herculaneum, the building was probably conceived as a pseudo-urban villa, that is as a residence place immediately outside the gates of the city.
Even if its space is clearly divided into *pars urbana, rustica* and *fructuaria,* in its final phase, the farming side of the villa was uppermost.
The excavation, undertaken between 1909 and 1910 by Aurelio Item who owned the land, continued from 1920 to 1930 when it was taken over by the State. We see here a grandiose four-sided building, built on an east-west axis, distinguished by a three-pronged *cryptoporticus* which creates a suspended area with panoramic rooms, preceded by colonnades and a garden.
The original layout of the house goes back to the second century B.C.
The sharply sloping terrain on which it was built was corrected by the construction of an artificial *podium*: the three-pronged *cryptoporticus* which supported the roof garden on three sides. In 70–60 B.C., the villa assumed a more complicated layout, when new areas were added and the *pars urbana* near the atrium was restructured. It was in this phase that the great wall-painting, which gives its name to the villa, was executed.
Other radical improvements occurred after the earthquake of 62 A.D., an event which probably marked the owners' departure from the villa. At the time of the eruption, the whole building was in a state of neglect (fig. 1), while construction works were being carried out. The master's quarters were uninhabited and bare, and life was concentrated in the rustic ones on the east side of the villa. Here, by halving some rooms, new spaces were being created, with a consequent rethinking of the function of the rooms.
The building work, far from being completed, had been entrusted by the last owners – the ancient family of the Istacidi – to the supervision of their freedman steward, *L. Istacidus Zosimus*, who has been identified thanks to a bronze seal found in one of the servants' rooms. From then on, the complex became a real *villa rustica,* aimed at the cultivation of agricultural products. Wine-making was clearly of greatest importance, as we can see from the large *torculum* found in the north-east part of the building.
Here, too, the eruption had driven the people living in the house at the time – the slaves and the workmen – to seek refuge on the upper floor: a muddled heap of ash, bones and rubble has yielded, in room 54, the bodies of three of the nine victims found in the villa, who had been thrown down the lower floor when the roofs and the attics collapsed under the weight of the lapilli.
The identification of the skeletons with two women and a baby girl is due to the discovery of four armbands, a necklace of gold and emerald (fig. 2) and three rings (figs. 3, 4) which, along with a mirror and a hoard of coins contained in a little cloth bag, formed the victims' treasures. [A. C.]

The
of t

There
tions
make
discuss
from t
and r
model
triclini
claim t
the diff
right to
tral sce
the sce
converg
figures
from tin
ed that t
a woma
ac myst
episodes
most re
the Fren
that it sh
left, show
wedding
good fan
married
the centra
of Dionys

1. Marble s
of a standi
dressed in
(*stola*) and
in a cloak (
It was foun
temporarily
up against t
of the colo
of the peris
and original
depicted a m
of the Istaci
(*Istacidia Ru*
in her sacerd
robes. Subse
it was adapte
to look like
Augustus' wi
SAP 4400
Augustan per
head from Ti
period

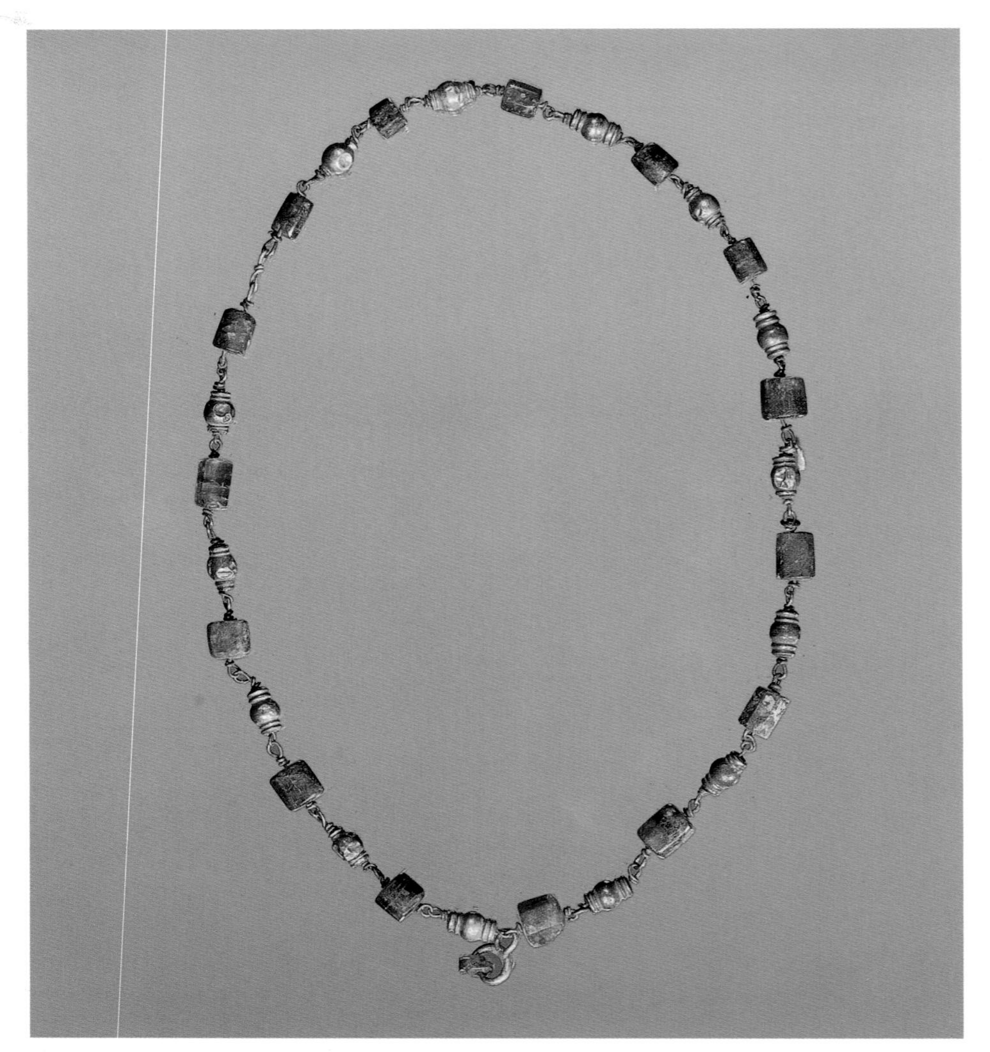

2. Gold and emerald necklace made up of alternating cylindrical emerald beads with hollow oval segments in gold foil, and enriched with a pendant in the form of a *lunula,* with an emerald prism fixed between its horns
SAP 4484
Early Imperial era

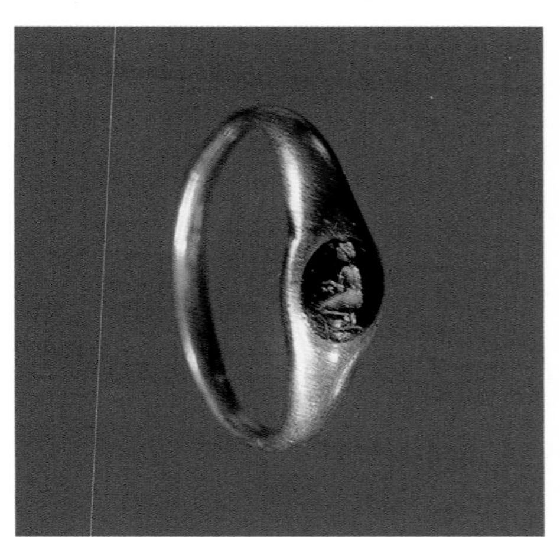

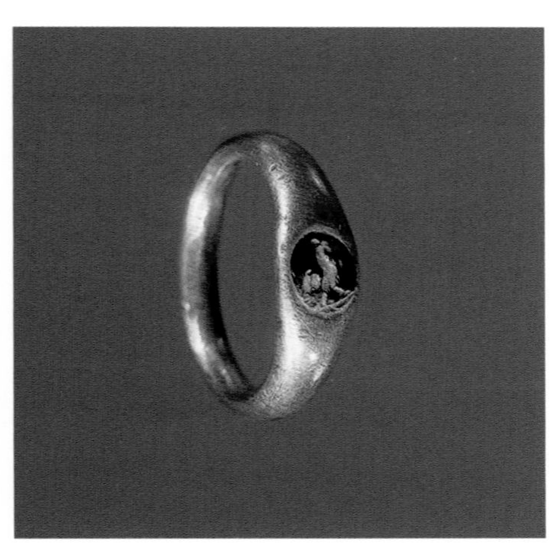

3, 4. Pair of rings with *prasium.* The narrow closed band contains, within an oval bezel, a *prasium*, with a slightly convex surface; in the first case (4487a) a nude crouching female figure in left-hand profile is engraved (Venus?), in the second (4487b), a cock strutting to the right, his wings partially spread
SAP 4487a, 4487b
Early Imperial era

THE HOUSE OF THE MENANDER (I, 10, 4)

A fresco depicting the Greek poet, found in an exedra on the peristyle, has given the name to this house which was excavated between 1926 and 1932.
It is one of the city's most prestigious *domus*, as we can tell from the size and layout of the rooms – master's quarters with baths and reception rooms, slaves' quarters, stables – and their decoration. The main entrance opens onto a lane which leads to the Via Stabiana and the house, as it stands at the time of the eruption, is the result of subsequent expansions which, starting from the end of the third century B.C. increased its size to approximately 1700 square metres. Here, too, rebuilding work was going on in August 79 A.D. The reception rooms were stripped, everyday furnishings were stacked in some of the rooms; some few precious objects were put for the time being where they would not get too much in the way or damaged, such as a marble statue of Apollo (fig. 1), originally in the garden, which had been moved under the colonnade; two triclinia (dining couches) (fig. 2) which had been dismantled and stacked in the *tablinum* and a brazier (fig. 3) which had been abandoned in the peristyle.
Final confirmation of the fact that the house was in a state of disruption on account of the building works comes from the discovery of two wooden boxes (hidden in an underground passage in the bath quarters) in which the family treasure had been stashed away. They contained jewels, gold and silver coins – of an overall value of 1432 sesterces, an average-size amount of ready cash for a rich Pompeian family – and the family silverware, comprising one hundred and eighteen embossed pieces of silver (both the *argentum escarium* and *potorium* as well as the *argentum balneare),* found wrapped in pieces of canvas and wool, of an overall weight of 24 kilos.
The rich owner of the house, Quintus Poppeus, who was joined by family links to *Poppaea Sabina*, Nero's second wife, was obviously not living in the house at the time of the eruption and had entrusted the renovation work to his own freedman steward, whose seal, *Quintus Poppeus Eros*, has been found.
It is likely that the skeleton which was discovered, along with that of a girl, in the cubicle of a little apartment inside the large house, belongs to him. The rain of lapilli which fell ceaselessly on Pompeii during the afternoon and night of 24th August rapidly filled the open spaces and those rooms of the house which had an *impluvium,* forcing the people who lived there,

or who had
there, to try
on the uppe
ten people, a
knocked do
with the hel
their few wr
(a couple of
a hook, whic
useful in the
to make thei
stones, which
the entrance
upper floor c
there to atter
Two women,
(fig. 4), mana
which opene
but were una
were overwhe
with the child
A third group
a woman amc
who carried a
him in a little
trying to oper
through the th
pickaxe and h

Silver Tableware

Silverware (*ministerium*) was composed of pieces of both functional and decorative use which the owner proudly showed off to his guests. Those designed to hold, serve and receive food, such as plates, dishes, casserole dishes, egg-cups and spoons, of various sizes and functions, were known as the *argentum escarium*, while those receptacles intended for mixing, pouring and drinking liquids, such as goblets, glasses, ladles, strainers and jugs, made up the *argentum potorium*. Most important among these were the goblets and cups, always in pairs and decorated with scenes which complemented each other, such as those on the *skyphoi* from Villa 2 at Terzigno. Such decorations no doubt prompted lively and learned conversations during dinner banquets. [A. C.]

1. Marble statue of Apollo. Characterized by Archaic features, the god is perhaps holding in his bent left arm a now lost lyre. With his downstretched arm he is stroking a griffin which leans against his leg
MANN 146103
First century A.D.

2. Bronze dining couch with wooden parts restored. On the wooden frame are bronze elements: modelled feet, strips at the corners and decoration at the sides (*fulcra*) of the headboard. On the main side, the *fulcrum* is decorated with a medallion of a bust of Silenus, and on the other with the head of a duck
SAP 4270a
First century A.D.

3. Bronze and iron cylindrical brazier with three lion-paw feet on modelled bases, and attachments decorated with a filigree palmette motif bearing a lion's face in the centre. The outer side is furnished with horizontal struts and has three lion's faces with handles inserted in them for carrying purposes
SAP 20315
First century A.D.

4. G
incis
The
of th
band
a flat
corn
with
(Pega
to th
MAN
First

THE HOUSE OF THE CRAFTSMAN (I, 10, 7)

This house, a modest two-storey dwelling of Sarno limestone which has a narrow and irregular ground-plan, is wedged in between a textile workshop and the House of the Menander, to which at one time it was attached.
In the centre of the house, excavated between December 1932 and February 1933, is a garden with a summer triclinium, onto which open the only two residential rooms worthy of comment. The discovery of numerous tools (fig. 1) piled in the portico which opened onto the garden and others (fig. 2) scattered in various rooms has suggested that this was the house-*cum*-workshop of a craftsman who specialised in working wood and metal.
Near the tools many metal and bone decorations have been found, for furniture and caskets and fastening devices for cases. The artisan's family doubtless lived with him: the jewels found in the atrium and in the *tablinum* are clearly those belonging to a woman (fig. 3).
Here, too, the impact of the eruption forced the inhabitants to seek shelter in the inmost part of the house, namely the triclinium which opened on the left side of the portico.
Here two people had sought refuge; an adult, who was discovered on the floor, his arms clutching the edge of a dining couch, and a second, younger, victim his arms folded under the head and legs stretched out on the floor.
On the ground, between the adult's feet, lay a little cloth bag containing a small hoard of twenty-six silver coins, amounting to just 104 sesterces.
In the triclinium another little heap of forty-eight coins was found, perhaps also the savings of one of the victims.
[A. C.]

1. Iron hoe (*ligo*) with trapezoidal blade, and slot to accommodate the wooden handle, of which traces remain
SAP 18228
First century A.D.

2. Long, narrow, iron hatchet (*securis*) of trapezoidal shape with rectilinear blade. Part of the wooden handle is still in its slot
SAP 18227
First century A.D.

T

Pon
of t
liver
Sho
and
the
ofte
shop
woo
Ther
prod
ducti
bread
weig
bakin
of *gar*
ing t
marke
tion c
can fo
ing o
the ta
rum),
washi
the ite
garme
by the
nally,
utensil
the iro
ius Jun
Zosimu

3. Heavy gold chain with figure-of-eight links, snake-head fastening and pendant featuring a statuette of Isis Fortuna, holding a rudder and cornucopia
SAP 5413
First century A.D.

THE LARGE PALAESTRA (II, 7)

The Large Palaestra (142 × 110 metres), a public building situated in the south-east part of the city walls, near the Amphitheatre, was built in the Augustan period, principally as a gymnasium for the youth of Pompeii who until then had to make do with the small palaestra of the Stabian Baths.
The layout of the Palaestra, closed off internally with three colonnades of a hundred columns, included a large swimming pool (*natatio*) in the centre.
After the excavation of the Quadriporticus of the Theatres, between 1935 and 1939 the largest number of victims was found in this area, almost one hundred bodies, sixty-five of which were found in the pumice layer and the rest in the debris left by the final two surges (4 and 5) that hit the city.
It is reasonable to suppose that as the pumice fell, the Palaestra was either empty or traversed by the fugitives running through its colonnades, trying to reach the Nocera Gate. The large number of people found in the ash layers deposited by the surges is most likely to be connected with Pompeians trying to flee the city – especially those resident in *Regiones* II and III – who chose to escape in the direction of Nocera at dawn on 25th August, when activity from the volcano seemed to have reached a standstill.

Most of the victims fall into three large groups – we cannot tell whether they were related or just partners in flight – with only a few by themselves.
For some of them it is possible to reconstruct their 'stories' and hazard a guess at their identities by looking at the objects they carried or the imprints they left in the ash.
The first fourteen victimes, found near the central entrance on the east side, was split into two groups, both of them made up of young people and adults, and for this reason presumably family-related; only two people among them were carrying things. A woman, who was found lying on her back in the first group of six victims and who was wearing a large and heavy silver armband (fig. 1) and an iron ring, was making her escape with a silver *simpulum* and with a hoard of coins (one aureus and one hundred and thirty-one silver denarii) which she kept in a little wooden case, the lock of which was under her pelvis. The other person, a man from the second group of eight fugitives, had fallen face-down on the ground and had under him a little wooden box (*theca vulneraria)* – visible from the imprint – in which he kept the tools of his trade. Here we have a series of surgical instruments and different size bronze cylinders used for medicaments

(figs. 2-4). A
the followin
discovery: "T
who fled tak
with him. Di
the idea that
to his compa
Among the i
found beyonc
the discovery
door carrying
decorated wit
notable. On t
he has general
as a 'servant o
the silverware
of the goddess
suggested that
an initiate in t
perhaps he car
House of Lore
the *praedia* of J
religious practi
taken place.
Only two casts
taken from all t
in the Palaestra
and the other, a
"the handsome
man, one of the
men from Cam
just made for ru
gasp of the race.
identified as an
of the discovery
of bronze strigils
by gymnasts. [T.

1. Gold and silver armband in the form of a coiled snake. The bracelet, which weighs an exceptional 500 grams is markedly different from others of its type
SAP 6131
First century A.D.

2, 3. Bronze surgical instruments
SAP 6124, 6127, 6128
First century A.D.

4. Different-sized bronze cases with lids, for containing medicaments
SAP 6127, 6129 a–e
First century A.D.

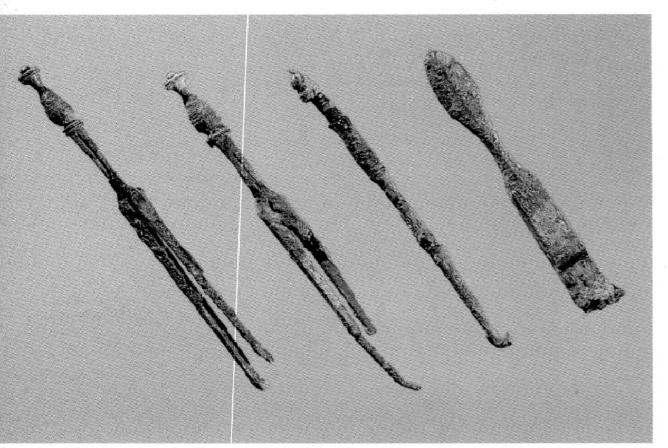

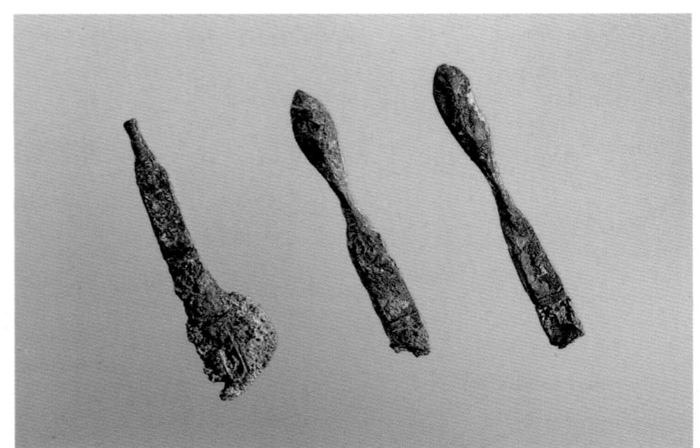

Ars Medica: Medicine and Surgery on the Slopes of Vesuvius

Celsus' treatise on medicine and surgery, *De Re Medica,* written in 30 B.C. shows the strong influence wielded by Greek medicine on Roman practice. The large number of instruments discovered in Pompeii and Herculaneum testifies to the widespread surgical practice.
At Pompeii, in the House of the Surgeon (VII, 1, 9.10.22), many instruments were found, including a conical catheter and a phlebotomist.
In a doctor's surgery in the Via dell'Abbondanza (VIII, 3,10.12) some instruments were likewise found, including a vaginal speculum – equipped with a turning mechanism which allowed the vagina to be opened – and a hook for extracting embryos.
Other instruments were found for example in the House of the Doctor (VIII, 5, 24) and in that of the New Doctor, as well as the very interesting cases on show in the exhibition (the doctor of the Large Palaestra and the one discovered among the fugitives who had taken shelter in Arcade 12 on the beach at Herculaneum).
Among the essential implements in a doctor's kit, we find above all probes, of different sizes, generally stored in a cylindrical container: spatulas, flat and spoon-shaped, all with different uses. Also essential were tweezers, forceps (for extracting teeth), lancets – remarkably similar to modern ones, with a smooth or indented handle to get a better grip, or with a curved blade for more delicate and precise incisions – and needles to sew up wounds with linen or woolen thread.
One particular type of needle, sharp but not too slender, was used in cataract operations to perforate the cornea and reach the crystalline lens. [T. R.]

6. Cast of a victim found near the latrine, crouching on the ground with his back against the wall of the east portico

THE PRAEDIA OF JULIA FELIX (II, 4, 3)

The monumental complex of the *praedia* – a term used to describe a property larger than an *insula* – was excavated mostly in 1755–57. This was the first systematic excavation of a building inside a city and not yet identified with ancient Pompeii. According to a custom used in the Bourbon period, the complex was stripped of its furniture and most valuable objects such as bronzes, marble and pictures, which were then sent to the Real Museo at Portici to enrich the collection of the royal family.

In the course of the excavations, an inscription was found on the façade of the building providing the name of the owner, Julia Felix, along with the notice advertising that she was letting her property, positioned so as to be highly visible to all who passed down the Via dell'Abbondanza, the busiest street of the city: "In the property of *Julia*, daughter of *Spurius Felix,* there is an elegant bath to let to respectable people, shops with living space above, first-floor apartments, from August 1st of the sixth year for five years, after which the contract is no longer valid."

In the economic crisis which followed the earthquake of 62 A.D. Julia Felix, in entrepreneurial spirit, was willing to let out a large part of her property, which in the meantime she had remodelled to fit its new function.

Her initiative came in response to the Pompeians' demand for new housing, after the destruction of many buildings and for hot baths, since the public ones were still under construction.

Immediately after the building was discovered and despoiled of its treasures, it was covered up again: when excavations were resumed between 1951–52, the whole complex came to light, enabling scholars to distinguish between the public part of the house, with its own entrance, and the private one.

From the monumental entrance that opened onto Via dell'Abbondanza, clients proceeded to the colonnaded courtyard equipped with seats, which served as a waiting room. From here they went to the *frigidarium*, *tepidarium*, *laconicum*, and *calidarium*.

In the courtyard a swimming pool was also discovered, which could be reached through the next-door *taberna* as well. We can tell that Julia Felix was a wealthy woman, not only from the renovation work of the public part of her house, but also from the construction of the elegant portico with fluted marble columns which sheltered the summer triclinium. The generosity and euergetism of the owners in financing restorations of parts of the Forum after the 62 A.D. earthquake is confirmed – as some

scholars mai
in the house
(fig. 1) – on
In the face c
outlay, "it wa
not wait, wh
her any retur
at a time wh
and manpow
all her good
into the air"
Near the gar
decorated wi
which a clay
(fig. 2) – the
was found wh
a little box cc
two pairs of e
a necklace wi
and an emera
possible that t
since the jewe
an affluent soc
people were t
her, while a g
headed by a n
and an iron ri
of his servile s
the *procurator* (
was trying to
entrance. The
put a stop to a

1. Fresco belonging to the middle section of a Fourth-style wall-painting, with Dionysiac cult objects. On steps leading up to a stage a tambourine, a basket with *rhython* and panther-skin, a *kalyx* and a *thyrsus* are depicted. On the right is a silver *kantharos* and two cymbals, and in the foreground a panther attacking a snake
MANN 8795
First century A.D.

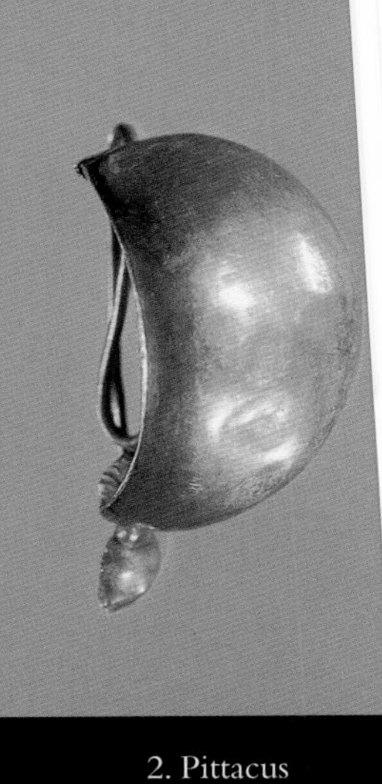

2. Pittacus of Mitilene, one of the seven wise men of Archa Greece, is represented as an o man with a scroll in his right hand. This clay statue, the work of a Campanian workshop, is part of a series of terra-cotta sculptures which were to decorate gardens with 'intellectual' themes
SAP 20595
First century A.D.

4. Gold chain necklace of the 'loop-in-loop' type bearing small pearls, fastening with an uncut emerald, and pendant in the shape of a *lunula*
SAP 8608
First century B.C.–first century A.D.

THE HARBOUR GATE

The large projection with square turrets, standing out from the line of the city walls, opens half-way up the western slope on which Pompeii extends.
The Harbour Gate was the last one to be constructed, and consists of a two-lane barrel-vaulted tunnel which gave a wider access for vehicles and a narrower one for pedestrians. The road to the sea departed from here, flanked on the stretch immediately behind the city walls, by wealthy houses and by the so-called Suburban Baths, laid out on a series of man-made terraces. And it was down this pedestrian access, at the first light of dawn on August 25th, that two women tried to make their escape. The body of the first one, who was not carrying any objects, was found with her head turned towards the sea, a few metres from the Suburban Baths. The second one lay at a little distance. The portico wall bordering the ground in front of the Baths, knocked down by the violence of the final surge, had collapsed on top of her, although she was already dead.
Next to her were a pair of gold earrings and most likely belonging to her were a few coins, three rings with gemstones (fig. 1) and three pairs of gold earrings (fig. 2) as well as a statuette of Mercury (fig. 3) found near the same wall.
[A. C.]

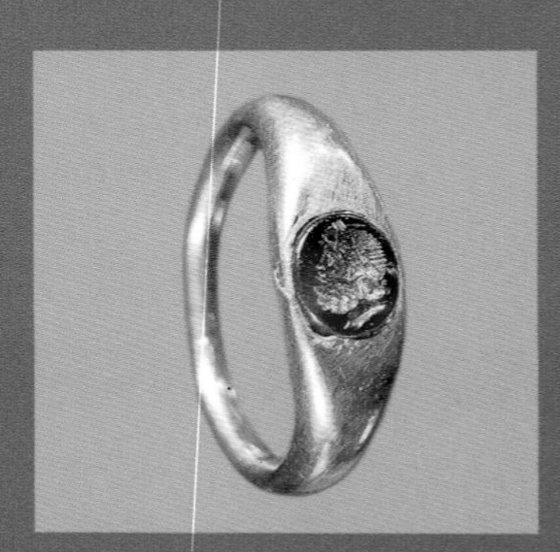

1. Gold ring with engraved cornelian. The hollow band contains a flat-surfaced cornelian in a bezel, on which a bearded and garlanded male head (Jupiter?) is carved in left-hand profile
SAP 12520
First century A.D.

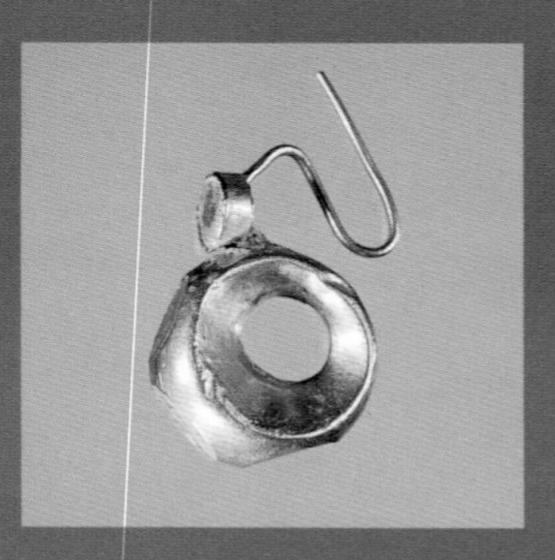

2. Crescent-shaped gold earrings. On the smooth moulded circular frame and where the hook is attached are oval bezels containing white and green glass paste
SAP 12518
First century A.D.

3. Silver and gold statuette of Mercury. The god is standing, with a gold diadem on his head and a *bulla* round his neck; he is nude apart from a cloak which hangs from his shoulders and is wound around his left arm. In his right hand he holds a little sack on a ram's head; in his left hand he grasps the caduceus
SAP 12523
First century A.D.

THE HOUSE OF THE GOLDEN BRACELET

The house of the Golden Bracelet was built on three levels and looked out over the sea along the panoramic western slope of the city. It was part of a grand building complex which was excavated in the 1960s and attributed entirely to the Fabis Rufus family on the basis of the discovery of a signet-ring, some inscriptions and graffiti.
However, the resumption of excavations in the 1980s has allowed to define the living space to the north of the House of Fabius Rufus as a separate dwelling; it takes its name – the House of the Golden Bracelet – from the discovery of a large piece of gold jewellery (fig. 1) of exceptional weight (610 grams) and of unusual design, which decorated the arm of one of the victims found in the house, identifiable as a rich matron (perhaps the owner of the building?).
The upper floor which has the typical *domus* plan – a Tuscan atrium surrounded by cubicles, triclinia and the *ala* – was connected by a staircase to the floor beneath: this was the undeniably luxurious part of the house, with reception rooms, among which triclinia, and a private bath suite.
Another staircase led to the second floor below, which opened on the summer triclinium – decorated with splendid garden scenes – and the bedroom, both facing onto a garden with a central fountain, a pergola and paths at the side.
The excavation of the garden has yielded a large quantity of fragments of late Third-style paintings, although these were no longer in situ, having belonged to a room which had since been redecorated. In this exhibition, for the first time, a wall fresco (figs. 2–7) is on display – reconstructed from the mass of fragments. Within a refined decorative scheme, a central picture shows three figures: a male figure wearing an ivy wreath (a poet?), a female figure reading a diptych (a poetess?) and a boy with *oinochoe* and plate for offerings. The high quality of the fresco indicates a more refined clientele than the following phase, to which one can attribute

the choice
who carri
paintings (
of 62 A.D.)
inferior. C
are the pict
and Ariadn
and Roxan
in the last p
of the hous
Pompeians
of the disco
quantity of
(among the
and more th
silver denari
scattered – p
a wooden ca
of the house
to one of the
at the foot o
to the garden
A little famil
by a couple a
one of whom
– whose casts
in the show –
the stairs of t
collapsed and

1. Gold bracelet of exceptional weight (610 grams), in the form of a two-headed snake. In its jaws the reptile holds a gold disc on which is the bust of Silenus in relief, surmounted by a crescent moon and seven stars
MANN 14268
First century A.D.

2. Dining room. Central picture of the fresco depicting three people: on the left, a male figure with an ivy wreath (a poet?), in the centre a boy with *oinochoe* and offering plate, on the right a female figure (a poetess?)
SAP 86075
30–35 A.D.

3. Dining room.
Detail from
the fresco depicting
a garden; from
the branches hang
Dionysiac symbols,
(Satyr, Silenus, pan
pipes, *situla*, *phallus*,
goat's head)
SAP 86075
30–35 A.D.

4. Dining room.
Detail of a fresco
with Maenads, Satyrs
and Silenus
in a meadow
SAP 8075
30–35 A.D.

5. Dining room.
Upper section with
picture showing
a couple and
maidservant
SAP 86076
30–35 A.D.

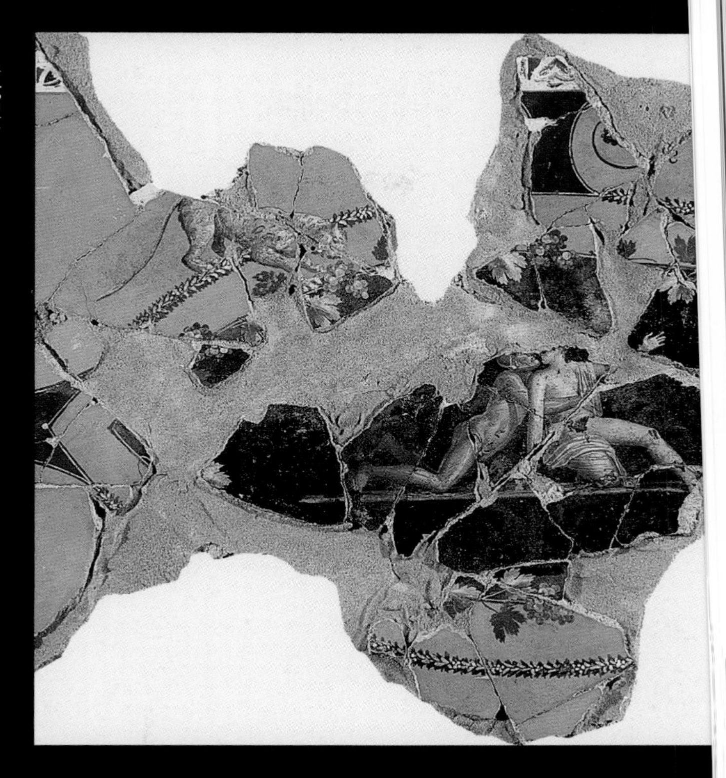

6. Dining room.
Upper section with
oval picture showing
Silenus with Maenad
SAP 86077
30–35 A.D.

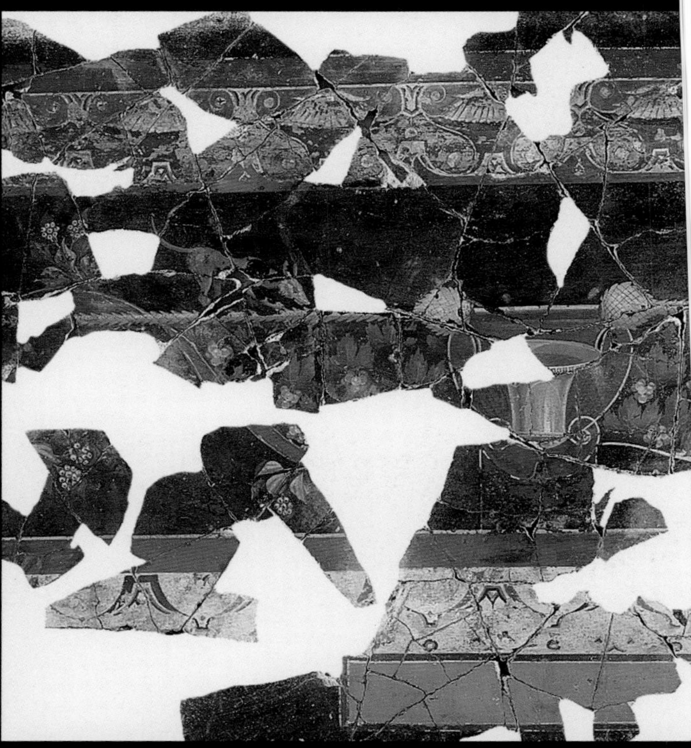

7. Dining room.
Fragment of border
with depiction
of *kantharos*
and greyhounds
SAP 86078
30–35 A.D.

s of victims:
oup
g
ults
children,
em
who died
e house

10. Cast of a child, part of the family group found under the staircase

THE HOUSE OF JULIUS POLYBIUS (IX, 13, 1-

Excavated between 1966 and 1978, the house faces onto Via dell'Abbondanza and has an almost rectangular ground-plan; with its almost 900 square metres surface, it occupies a stretch of ground which had remained unbuilt before the years between the third and the second century B.C. The layout of the numerous rooms is divided into two clearly-marked sectors, one for the masters and one for the slaves, to which an upper floor was added in the second century B.C. The two parts are linked by a square garden – at the time of the eruption it was planted as an orchard – with colonnades on three sides, flanked by the most representative rooms. The house, which underwent minor improvements in the course of time, belonged in 79 A.D. to a family of Imperial freedmen of Greek origin: election slogans on nearby walls and at the entrance urge people to vote for *C. Iulius Polybius*, while in one of the wooden cupboards located under the garden portico a bronze seal was found, probably belonging to the owner of the house, *C. Iulius Philippus*.
This house also experienced serious damage from the earthquake which preceded the eruption and here too, repair work was underway, as we can see from the heap of lime near the entrance. However, it was not abandoned: everywhere were objects of daily use; the cupboards in the peristyle held everyday tableware and the kitchen continued to function. The only precaution which the master seemed to have taken was to keep some antique bronze articles locked up safe in the triclinium: a statue of Apollo, for example (fig. 3), reused as a lamp stand; a *kalyx* crater (fig. 1) which can be dated to the second century B.C., decorated with a procession of armed men, figures from myth; a dinner-set, candelabra stands and three dining couches with bronze feet and decorations: objects belonging to a family of a middle-to-high economic level, even if of a mediocre social status. When the first phase of the eruption descended on Pompeii,

perhaps afte
of the room
the people l
at the time (
who had sta
the building
themselves?)
of the buildi
roofs had not
in two adjace
and a dining
found, three c
and babies –
other. As they
for the erupti
stretched out
others on the
they were kill
of the surge. S
of money, mer
Among them
between sixtee
old, now in the
of pregnancy, p
to the owner's
She was wearin
and clutching a
with her small s
and silver coins.

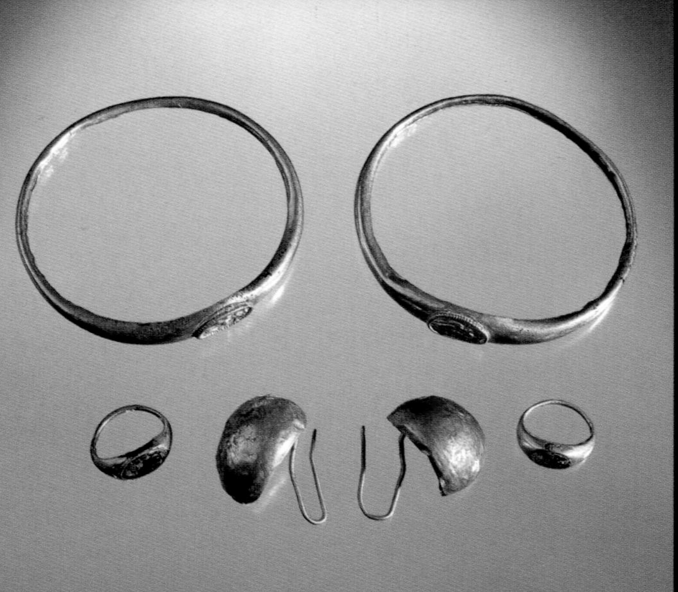

1. Bronze *kalyx* crater, resting on a stand decorated with lanceolate leaves and palmettes in very low relief.
The central part of the crater is taken up with a relief frieze, on which male figures bearing weapons – six standing, two seated – are depicted with some animals, among them two dogs and a horse
SAP 45180
Second century B.C.

2. This pair of armbands with decorated relief setting, the hook earrings with spherical segments, and the two rings with engraved stones made up the *parure* of the young pregnant woman who died in the triclinium
SAP 23878–23879–2387–23876–23877
First century A.D.

3. Head of bronze statue of Apollo.
The god is in a standing position with his left leg slightly forward; his arms are folded with his right hand open and his left clenched in a fist.
The eyes are of ivory (the cornea) and glass paste (the iris and the pupil).
The statue underwent restoration in ancient times and was later turned into a lamp stand by placing a marble shelf on the arms
SAP 22924
First century A.D.

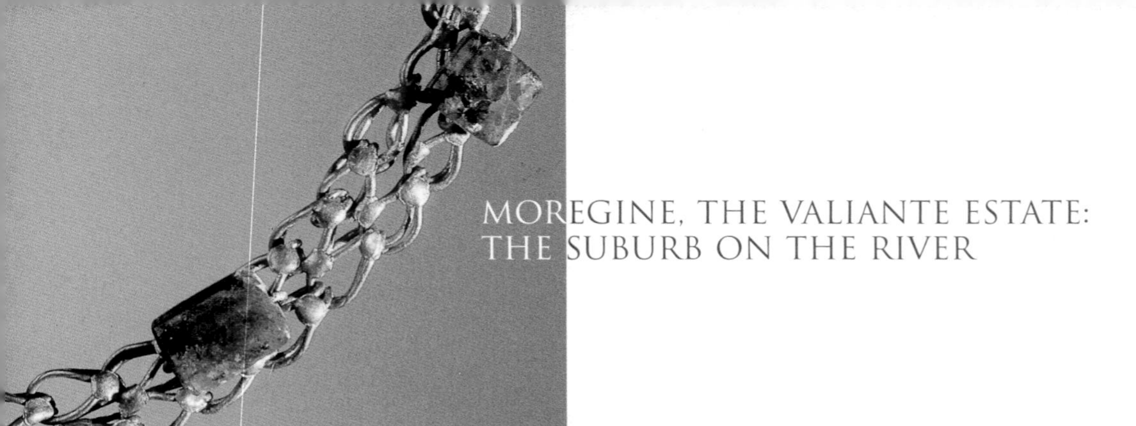

MOREGINE, THE VALIANTE ESTATE: THE SUBURB ON THE RIVER

At the end of the nineteenth century, on the estate of Baron Valiante, in the district of Moregine to the south of Pompeii, some buildings were brought to light about 600 metres from one of the gates of Pompeii – the Stabian Gate – along with a large number of fugitives who were carrying objects of varying value. Further research revealed that this was actually a multi-storeyed building, partly divided up into small independent living spaces decorated with Fourth-style frescoes and partly into rustic-type rooms used for storage. A second large building of similar design and other structures stretched out beyond an alley. This group of buildings has been interpreted as a residential and commercial suburb, placed in a strategic position for commercial trade along the waterways and roads. Indeed, this area was connected both with the road – which started at the Stabian Gate and ran from Pompeii towards Stabia – and with the river Sarno, the ancient course of which is believed to have been located in a depression near the buildings. The quarter by the Sarno was probably a *vicus*, as the finds on display suggest: a fresco depicting a scene of sacrifice to the Lares Compitales and some clay statuettes of figures wearing togas, the *vicomagistri*. Inside the rooms and outside the buildings many groups of people have been found, many of whom carrying only a few coins and jewellery pieces typical of the Vesuvius area; it is very likely that some lived in the buildings and others had escaped from nearby Pompeii.

Four fugitives, found near a staircase, stand out among all these groups of victims, for their riches, money and the value of the objects they carried. Here we have two stunning broad gold necklaces with pearls and emeralds (figs. 1, 2), two gold bracelets with eight little ovals (fig. 3), and a considerable hoard of twelve gold coins and a hundred and eight silver coins, as well as silver and iron jewellery. [T. R.]

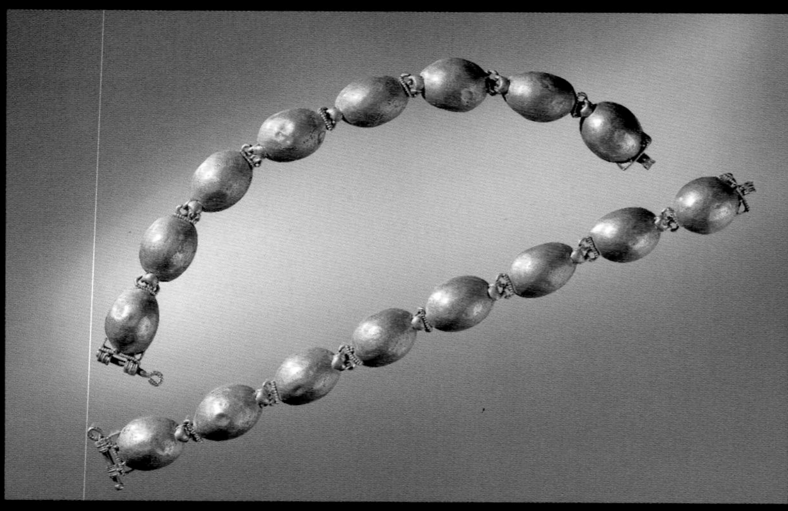

2. Broad necklace of gold wire chain, on which fourteen cylindrical plasma stones are threaded
MANN 114288
First century B.C.–first century A.D.

3. Pair of gold bracelets with elongated hemispheres, threaded on chains of knurled wire
MANN 114317–114318
First century B.C.–first century A.D.

MOREGINE: THE BUILDING OF THE TRIC

In the course of construction work to make a third lane on the A3 autostrada, in the stretch between Castellammare di Stabia and Scafati, a complex of buildings has recently been discovered at Moregine, south of Pompei, in an area first excavated in 1959 and already famous for the discovery of a hundred and twenty-five wax-tablets relating to the business deals of the *Sulpicii* family. The house has two sections: the portico of the triclinia and the bath suite which was later added to the first.
The recent exploration has enabled the north section of the building to be uncovered and subsequently detach and restore the wonderful frescoes decorating the three newly found rooms. This important building, which houses at its core three triclinia, is walled in on three sides in *opera reticulata.* At the time of their discovery, the dining rooms, each closed off by a sliding wooden screen on a pair of wheels, still had their dining couches, clad in marble, and the circular table in the middle. To complete the luxury of the furnishings – of the couches and the rooms – and the advanced hydraulic technology, the triclinia also displayed wall-paintings of an extraordinary high quality. The decorative schemes run as follows. In the west triclinium (A) (figs. 1–3) inside a refined architectonic framework against a red background, we see Apollo Citharoedus surrounded by the Muses: Euterpe with double flute, Muse of dance and tragic choruses; Clio with her written scroll, Muse of history; Calliope with diptych and pen, Muse of lyric poetry; Terpsichore with the cithara, Muse of cerimonial song; Thalia with comic mask and crook, Muse of comedy; Melpomene, Muse of tragedy with tragic mask and club; Urania with heavenly globe and *virgula,* Muse of astronomy. The central triclinium (B) (fig. 4) depicts the Dioscuri against a black background. One is pictured wearing a tunic and the other in athletic nudity, both holding their horses by the bridles. This is the worst preserved wall-painting. The east triclinium (C), according to a similar decorative scheme, shows a personified river god (Sarno?) or more probably of a marsh, with different offerers on pedestals and winged Victories with attributes of Athena and Apollo (figs. 5–7). Marisa Mastroroberto's recent research into the fresco-cycle of Moregine suggests a connection between the themes and motifs on the wall-paintings and the emperor Nero, as well as defining a link between the emperor and the actual function of the building. Perhaps here we have one of the *tabernae deversoriae,* i.e. one of the staging posts which

were built s
and coasts c
to accomm
on his trave
About 100
of the tricli
on the right
a second bu
In this, vario
functional; in
in one of th
of two adult
women were
a girl of four
years old. O
women, who
was found lyi
on the floor,
jewellery in h
(figs. 8–11): sh
two armbands
and was carry
bag (*sacculus*) a
two rings, a n
and a *catena.* C
among this co
is an armband
inscription DO
which brings c
relationships b
and their slave-
as prostitutes. [

1. Triclinium A. Fresco from the north wall, with depiction of Apollo
SAP 85182
First century A.D.

um A.
m the east
depiction
use Thalia
3
ury A.D.

3. Triclinium A.
Fresco from the west
wall with depiction
of the Muse Calliope
SAP 85181
First century A.D.

clinium C. Fresco
the west wall
ting, in the centre,
ory with shield,
and Corinthian
et
85187
century A.D.

7. Triclinium C. Fresco from the north wall with allegory of The Marsh

explicit erotic content, ell-known *Veneris figurae*, in stone beds and graffi- the names and prices of offered, would seem to house at *Regio* VII, 12, othel – perhaps the only from the ancient world. es to those found in the g with stone beds and een discovered in many Pompeii, and there is fur- gical evidence for pros- iquity. We find such ev- lic places such as *caupon-* and also in the public y sources state that in the ishments, not only the lso the mistress was in- stitution. An inscription recording the expenses y one client, also men- owed to the *puella*.

other ancient texts reveal s employed in the dress- lent themselves to pros- rescoes in the Suburban e of the Harbour Gate reted in this light.

ctions of explicit erotic from private houses as rom those of notable these, we must suppose er of the house used his sexual services. In these ng to the standards of is not really prostitution n sense. Indeed, Roman master to use his slaves manner he wished, in- ex. But if such things thin the context of a pri- n a public place, such as at the baths, it did not ostitution' as such, with nying degradation for l.

locations of frescoes of content casts light onto rea of slave activity in r Giovanni Guzzo]

8. Gold armband with thick band, in the form of a snake with glass paste eyes. The inscription DOM(I)NUS ANCILLAE SUAE, quite a rarity on jewellery, identifies the bracelet as the gift of a master to his slave-girl
SAP 81580
First century A.D.

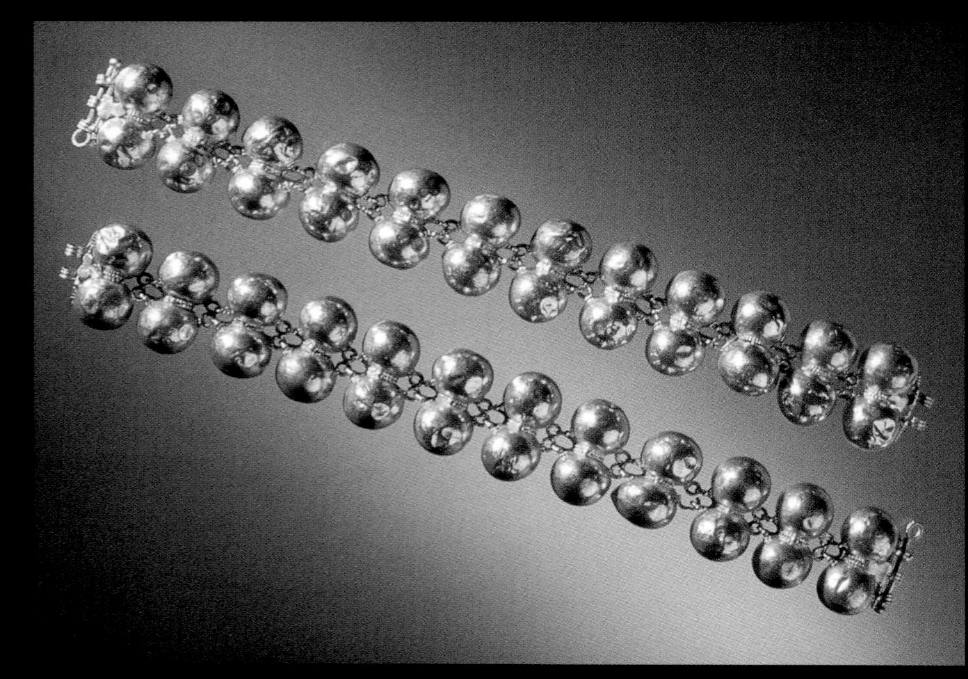

9. Gold bracelets with pairs of hollow hemispheres, onto which gold foil vine-leaves are soldered
SAP 81584
First century A.D.

11. Go
neckla
of-eig
and ho
with a
in the
of a cr
SAP 8
First ce

ENT SOURCES O

Letters by Pliny the Younger to Tacitus

C. PLINIUS TACITO SUO S.

Petis, ut tibi avunculi mei exitum scribam, quo verius trader
gratias ago; nam video morti eius, si celebretur a te, immorta
esse propositam. quamvis enim pulcherrimarum clade terraru
ut urbes, memorabili casu quasi semper victurus occiderit, qua
opera et mansura condiderit, multum tamen perpetuitati eius
tuorum aeternitas addet. equidem beatos puto, quibus deorum
aut facere scribenda aut scribere legenda, beatissimos vero, qui
horum in numero avunculus meus et suis libris et tuis erit. q
deposco etiam, quod iniungis.

Erat Miseni classemque imperio praesens regebat. nonum Kal
fere septima mater mea indicat ei apparere nubem inusitata et
et specie. usus ille sole, mox frigida, gustaverat iacens studebat
ascendit locum, ex quo maxime miraculum illud conspici poter
incertum procul intuentibus, ex quo monte (Vesuvium fuisse p
oriebatur, cuius similitudinem et formam non alia magis arbor
expresserit. nam longissimo velut trunco elata in altum quibus
diffundebatur, credo, quia recenti spiritu evecta, dein senescente
aut etiam pondere suo victa in latitudinem vanescebat, candida
interdum sordida et maculosa, prout terram cineremve sustulerat
Magnum propiusque noscendum, ut eruditissimo viro, visum. iu
aptari: mihi, si venire una vellem, facit copiam: respondi studere
et forte ipse, quod scriberem dederat. egrediebatur domo: accipit c
Rectinae Casci imminenti periculo exterritae (nam villa eius sub
nisi navibus fuga); ut se tanto discrimini eriperet, orabat. vertit i
quod studioso animo incohaverat, obit maximo. deducit quadrire
ipse non Rectinae modo, sed multis (erat enim frequens amoenita
laturus auxilium. properat illuc, unde alii fugiunt, rectumque curs
recta gubernacula in periculum tenet adeo solutus metu, ut omnis
mali motus, omnis figuras, ut deprenderat oculis, dictaret enotaretq
Iam navibus cinis incidebat, quo propius accederent, calidior et de
etiam nigrique et ambusti et fracti igne lapides, iam vadum subitu
montis litora obstantia. cunctatus paulum, an retro flecteret, mox g
ut ita faceret, monenti "fortes", inquit, "fortuna iuvat, Pomponian
Stabiis erat, diremptus sinu medio (nam sensim circumactis curvati
mare infunditur); ibi, quamquam nondum periculo appropinquante
tamen et, cum cresceret, proximo, sarcinas contulerat in naves certus
si contrarius ventus resedisset. quo tunc avunculus meus secundissi
invectus complectitur trepidantem, consolatur, hortatur, utque timore
eius sua securitate leniret, deferri in balineum iubet: lotus accubat, c
aut hilaris aut, quod aeque magnum, similis hilari.

Interim e Vesuvio monte pluribus locis latissimae flammae altaque i
relucebant, quorum fulgor et claritas tenebris noctis excitabatur. ille c
trepidatione ignes relictos desertasque villas per solitudinem ardere i
formidinis dictitabat. tum se quieti dedit et quievit verissimo quidem

nam meatus animae, qui illi propter amplitudinem corporis gravior et sonantior erat, ab iis, qui limini obversabantur, audiebatur. sed area, ex qua diaeta adibatur, ita iam cinere mixtisque pumicibus oppleta surrexerat, ut, si longior in cubiculo mora, exitus negaretur. excitatus procedit seque Pomponiano ceterisque, qui pervigilaverant, reddit. in commune consultant, intra tecta subsistant an in aperto vagentur. nam crebris vastisque tremoribus tecta nutabant et quasi emota sedibus suis nunc huc, nunc illuc abire aut referri videbantur. sub dio rursus quamquam levium exesorumque pumicum casus metuebatur; quod tamen periculorum collatio elegit. et apud illum quidem ratio rationem, apud alios timorem timor vicit. cervicalia capitibus imposita linteis constringunt; id munimentum adversus incidentia fuit.

Iam dies alibi, illic nox omnibus noctibus nigrior densiorque, quam tamen faces multae variaque lumina solabantur. placuit egredi in litus et ex proximo adspicere, ecquid iam mare admitteret, quod adhuc vastum et adversum permanebat. ibi super abiectum linteum recubans semel atque iterum frigidam poposcit hausitque. deinde flammae flammarumque praenuntius odor sulpuris alios in fugam vertunt, excitant illum. innitens servolis duobus adsurrexit et statim concidit, ut ego colligo, crassiore caligine spiritu obstructo clausoque stomacho, qui illi natura invalidus et angustus et frequenter interaestuans erat. ubi dies redditus (is ab eo, quem novissime viderat, tertius), corpus inventum integrum, inlaesum opertumque, ut fuerat indutus: habitus corporis quiescenti quam defuncto similior.

Interim Miseni ego et mater - sed nihil ad historiam, nec tu aliud quam de exitu eius scire voluisti. finem ergo faciam. unum adiciam: omnia me, quibus interfueram, quaeque statim, cum maxime vera memorantur, audieram, persecutum. tu potissima excerpes: aliud est enim epistulam, aliud historiam, aliud amico, aliud omnibus scribere. vale.

(Plinius Caecilus Secundus, *Epistulae*, VI, 16)

Gaius Plinius sends greetings to his friend Cornelius
Thank you for asking me to send you a description c
you can leave an accurate account of it for posterity;
awaits him if his death is recorded by you. It is true t
in a catastrophe which destroyed the loveliest regions
by whole cities and their people, and one so memorak
his name live for ever: and he himself wrote a numbe
but you write for all time and can still do much to pe
The fortunate man, in my opinion, is he to whom the
the power either to do something which is worth recc
is worth reading, and most fortunate of all is the man
Such a man was my uncle, as his own books and yours
So you set me a task I would choose for myself, an I a
to start on it.

My uncle was stationed at Misenum, in active comman
On 24th August, in the early afternoon, my mother dre
to a cloud of unusual size and appearance. He had bee
had taken a cold bath, and lunched while lying down, a
at his books. He called for his shoes and climbed up to
give him the best view of the phenomenon. It was not
from which mountain the cloud was rising (it was afterv
to be Vesuvius); its general appearance can best be expres
an umbrella pine, for it rose to a great height on a sort o
off into branches, I imagine because it was thrust upwarc
and then left unsupported as the pressure subsided, or els
by its own weight so that it spread out and gradually disp
it looked white, sometimes blotched and dirty, according
of oil and ashes it carried with it. My uncle's scholarly ac
that it was important enough for a close inspection, and h
to be made ready, telling me I could come with him if I
I preferred to go on with my studies, and as it happened h
me some writing to do.

As he was leaving the house he was handed a message fro
of Tascus whose house was at the foot of the mountain, so
was impossible except by boat. She was terrified by the da
her and implored him to rescue her from her fate. He cha
and what he had begun in a spirit of inquiry he completed
orders for the warships to be launched and went on board
the intention of bringing help to many more people beside
lovely stretch of coast was thickly populated. He hurried t
everyone else was hastily leaving, steering his course straigh
zone. He was entirely fearless, describing each new movem
of the portent to be noted down exactly as he observed the
already falling, hotter and thicker as the ships drew near, foll
of pumice and blackened stones, charred and cracked by the

suddenly they were in shallow water, and the shore was blocked by the debris from the mountain. For a moment my uncle wondered whether to turn back, but when the helmsman advised this he refused, telling him that Fortune stood by the courageous and they must make for Pomponianus at Stabiae.
He was cut off there by the breadth of the bay (for the shore gradually curves round a basin filled by the sea) so that he was not as yet in danger, though it was clear that this would come nearer as it spread. Pomponianus had therefore already put his belongings on board ship, intending to escape if the contrary wind fell. This wind was of course full in my uncle's favour, and he was able to bring his ship in. He embraced his terrified friend, cheered and encouraged him and thinking he could calm his fears by showing his own composure, gave orders that he was to be carried to the bathroom. After his bath he lay down and dined; he was quite cheerful, or at any rate he pretended he was, which was no less courageous.
Meanwhile on Mount Vesuvius broad sheets of fire and leaping flames blazed at several points, their bright glare emphasized by the darkness of night. My uncle tried to allay the fears of his companions by repeatedly declaring that these were nothing but bonfires left by the peasants in their terror, or else empty houses on fire in the districts they had abandoned. Then he went to rest and certainly slept, for as he was a stout man his breathing was rather loud and heavy and could be heard by people coming and going outside his door. By this time the courtyard giving access to his room was full of ashes mixed with pumice-stones, so that its level had risen, and if he had stayed in the room any longer he would never have got out. He was wakened, came out and joined Pomponianus and the rest of the household who had sat up all night. They debated whether to stay indoors or take their chance in the open, for the buildings were now shaking with violent shocks, and seemed to be swaying to and fro as if they were torn from their foundations. Outside on the other hand, there was the danger of falling pumice-stones, even though these were light and porous; however, after comparing the risks they chose the latter. In my uncle's case one reason outweighed the other, but for the others it was a choice of fears. As a protection against falling objects they put pillows on their heads tied down with cloths.
Elsewhere there was daylight by this time, but they were still in darkness, blacker and denser than any ordinary night, which they relieved by lighting torches and various kinds of lamps. My uncle decided to go down to the shore and investigate on the spot the possibility of any escape by sea, but he found the waves still wild and dangerous. A sheet was spread on the ground for him to lie down, and he repeatedly asked for cold water to drink. Then the flames and smell of sulphur which gave warning of the approaching fire drove the others to take flight and roused him to stand up. He stood leaning on two slaves and then suddenly collapsed, I imagine because the dense fumes choked his breathing by blocking his windpipe which was constitutionally weak and narrow and often inflamed.
When daylight returned on the 26th – two days after the last day he had seen –

his body was found intact and uninjured, still fully clc
like sleep than death.
Meanwhile my mother and I were at Misenum, but tl
interest, and you only wanted to hear about my uncle'
I will say no more, except to add that I have describec
which I either witnessed myself or heard about immec
when reports were most likely to be accurate. It is for
suits your purpose, for there is a great difference betwe
and history written for all to read.
(English translation by Betty Radice, *The Letters of the* Y
books, 1963)

C. PLINIUS TACITO SUO S.
Ais te adductum litteris, quas exigenti tibi de morte avunculi mei scripsi, cupere cognoscere, quos ego Miseni relictus (id enim ingressus abruperam) non solum metus, verum etiam casus pertulerim. "quamquam animus meminisse horret..., incipiam". Profecto avunculo ipse reliquum tempus studiis (ideo remanseram) impendi; mox balineum, cena, somnus inquietus et brevis. praecesserat per multos dies tremor terrae minus formidolosus, quia Campaniae solitus; illa vero nocte ita invaluit, ut non moveri omnia, sed verti crederentur. inrumpit cubiculum meum mater: surgebam invicem, si quiesceret, excitaturus. resedimus in area domus, quae mare a tectis modico spatio dividebat. dubito, constantiam vocare an imprudentiam debeam (agebam enim duodevicensimum annum): posco librum Titi Livi et quasi per otium lego atque etiam, ut coeperam, excerpo. ecce amicus avunculi, qui nuper ad eum ex Hispania venerat; ut me et matrem sedentis, me vero etiam legentem videt, illius patientiam, securitatem meam corripit. nihilo segnius ego intentus in librum.
Iam hora diei prima, et adhuc dubius et quasi languidus dies. iam quassatis circumiacentibus tectis, quamquam in aperto loco, angusto tamen, magnus et certus ruinae metus. tum demum excedere oppido visum; sequitur vulgus attonitum, quodque in pavore simile prudentiae, alienum consilium suo praefert ingentique agmine abeuntis premit et impellit. egressi tecta consistimus. multa ibi miranda, multas formidines patimur. nam vehicula, quae produci iusseramus, quamquam in planissimo campo, in contrarias partes agebantur ac ne lapidibus quidem fulta in eodem vestigio quiescebant. praeterea mare in se resorberi et tremore terrae quasi repelli videbamus. certe processerat litus multaque animalia maris siccis harenis detinebat. ab altero latere nubes atra et horrenda, ignei spiritus tortis vibratisque discursibus rupta in longas fiammarum figuras dehiscebat: fulguribus illae et similes et maiores erant.
Tum vero idem ille ex Hispania amicus acrius et instantius "si frater", inquit, "tuus, tuus avunculus vivit, vult esse vos salvos; si periit, superstites voluit. proinde quid cessatis evadere?" respondimus non commissuros nos, ut de salute illius incerti nostrae consuleremus. non moratus ultra proripit se effusoque cursu periculo aufertur.
Nec multo post illa nubes descendere in terras, operire maria: cinxerat Capreas et absconderat, Miseni quod procurrit, abstulerat. tum mater orare, hortari, iubere quoquo modo fugerem; posse enim iuvenem, se et annis et corpore gravem bene morituram, si mihi causa mortis non fuisset. ego contra: salvum me nisi una non futurum; dein manum eius amplexus addere gradum cogo. paret aegre incusatque se, quod me moretur.
Iam cinis, adhuc tamen rarus. respicio: densa caligo tergis imminebat, quae nos torrentis modo infusa terrae sequebatur. "deflectamus", inquam, "dum videmus, ne in via strati comitantium turba in tenebris obteramur". vix consideramus, et nox, non qualis inlunis aut nubila, sed qualis in locis clausis lumine exstincto. audires ululatus feminarum, infantum quiritatus, clamores virorum: alii parentes, alii liberos, alii coniuges vocibus requirebant, vocibus noscitabant; hi suum casum, illi suorum miserabantur; erant, qui metu mortis mortem precarentur; multi ad deos manus tollere, plures nusquam iam deos ullos aeternamque illam et novissimam noctem mundo interpretabantur. nec defuerunt, qui fictis mentitisque terroribus vera pericula

augerent. aderant qui Miseni illud ruisse, illud ardere falso, sed credentibus nuntiabant. paulum reluxit, quod non dies nobis, sed adventantis ignis indicium videbatur. et ignis quidem longius substitit, tenebrae rursus, cinis rursus multus et gravis. hunc identidem adsurgentes excutiebamus; operti alioqui atque etiam oblisi pondere essemus. possem gloriari non gemitum mihi, non vocem parum fortem in tantis periculis excidisse, nisi me cum omnibus, omnia mecum perire misero, magno tamen mortalitatis solacio credidissem.
Tandem illa caligo tenuata quasi in fumum nebulamve discessit; mox dies verus; sol etiam effulsit, luridus tamen, qualis esse, cum deficit, solet. occursabant trepidantibus adhuc oculis mutata omnia altoque cinere tamquam nive obducta. regressi Misenum curatis utcumque corporibus suspensam dubiamque noctem spe ac metu exegimus. metus praevalebat; nam et tremor terrae perseverabat, et plerique lymphati terrificis vaticinationibus et sua et aliena mala ludificabantur. nobis tamen ne tunc quidern, quamquam et expertis periculum et exspectantibus, abeundi consilium, donec de avunculo nuntius.
Haec nequaquam historia digna non scripturus leges et tibi, scilicet qui requisisti, imputabis, si digna ne epistula quidem videbuntur. vale.
(Plinius Caecilus Secundus, *Epistulae*, VI, 20)

Gaius Plinius sends greetings to his friend Cornelius Tacitus.
So the letter which you asked me to write on my uncle's death has made you eager to hear about the terrors and hazards I had to face when left at Misenum, for I broke off at the beginning of this part of my story. "Though my mind shrinks from remembering … I will begin."
After my uncle's departure I spent the rest of the day with my books, as this was my reason for staying behind. Then I took a bath, dined, and then dozed fitfully for a while. For several days past there had been earth tremors which were not particularly alarming because they are frequent in Campania: but that night the shocks were so violent that everything felt as if were not only shaken but overturned. My mother hurried into my room and found me already getting up to wake her if she were still asleep.
We sat down in the forecourt of the house, between the buildings and the sea close by. I don't know whether I should call this courage or folly on my part (I was only seventeen at the time) but I called for a volume of Livy and went on reading as if I had nothing else to do. I even went on with the extracts I had been making. Up came a friend of my uncle's who had just come from Spain to join him. When he saw us sitting there and me actually reading, he scolded us both – me for my foolhardiness and my mother for allowing it. Nevertheless, I remained absorbed in my book.
By now it was dawn, but the light was still dim and faint. The buildings round us were already tottering, and the open space we were in was too small for us not to be in real and imminent danger if the house collapsed. This finally decided us to leave the town. We were followed by a panic-stricken mob of people wanting to act on someone else's decision in preference to their own (a point in which fear looks like prudence), who hurried us on our way by pressing hard behind in a dense crown. Once beyond the buildings we stopped, and there we had some extraordinary experiences which thoroughly alarmed us. The carriages we had ordered to be brought out began to run in different directions though the ground was quite level, and would not remain stationary even when wedged with stones.
We also saw the sea sucked away and apparently forced back by the earthquake: at any rate it receded from the shore so that quantities of sea creatures were left stranded on dry sand. On the landward side a fearful black cloud was rent by forked and quivering bursts of flame, and parted to reveal great tongues of fire, like flashes of lightning magnified in size.
At this point my uncle's friend from Spain spoke up still more urgently: "If your brother, if your uncle is still alive, he will want you both to be saved; if he is dead, he would want you to survive him – why put off your escape?"
We replied that we would not think of considering our own safety as long as we were uncertain of his. Without waiting any longer, our friend rushed off and hurried out of danger as fast as he could.
Soon afterwards the cloud sank down to earth and covered the sea; it had already blotted out Capri and hidden the promontory of Misenum from sight. Then my mother implored, entreated and commanded me to escape

as best I could – a young man might escape, whereas she was old and slow and could die in peace as long as she had not been the cause of my death too. I refused to save myself without her, and grasping her hand forced her to quicken her pace. She gave in reluctantly, blaming herself for delaying me. Ashes were already falling, not as yet very thickly. I looked round: a dense black cloud was coming up behind us, spreading over the earth like a flood. "Let us leave the road while we can still see", I said, "or we shall be knocked down and trampled underfoot in the dark by the crowd behind."

We had scarcely sat down to rest when darkness fell, not the dark of a moonless or cloudy night, but as if the lamp had been put out in a closed room.

You could hear the shrieks of women, the wailing of infants, and the shouting of men; some were calling their parents, others their children or their wives, trying to recognise them by their voices. People bewailed their own fate or that of their relatives and there were some who prayed for death in their terror of dying. Many besought the aid of the gods, but still more imagined there were no gods left, and that the universe was plunged into eternal darkness for evermore. There were people, too, who added to the real perils by inventing fictitious dangers: some reported that part of Misenum had collapsed or another part was on fire, and though their tales were false they found others to believe them. A gleam of light returned, but we took this to be a warning of the approaching flames rather than daylight. However, the flames remained some distance off; then darkness came on once more and ashes began to fall again, this time in heavy showers. We rose from time to time and shook them off, otherwise we should have been buried and crushed beneath their weight. I could boast that not a groan or cry of fear escaped me in these perils, had I not derived some poor consolation in my mortal lot from the belief that the whole world was dying with me and I with it.

At last the darkness thinned and dispersed into smoke or cloud; then there was genuine daylight, and the sun actually shone out, but yellowish as it is during an eclipse. We were terrified to see everything changed, buried deep in ashes like snowdrifts. We returned to Misenum where we attended to our physical needs as best as we could, and then spent an anxious night alternating between hope and fear. Fear predominated, for the earthquakes went on, and several hysterical individuals made their own and other people's calamities seem ludicrous in comparison with their frightful predictions.

But even then in spite of the dangers we had been through and were still expecting, my mother and I had still no intention of leaving until we had news of my uncle.

Of course these details are not important enough for history, and you will read them without any idea of recording them; if they seem scarcely worth putting in a letter, you have only yourself to blame for asking for them.

(English translation by Betty Radice, *The Letters of the Younger Pliny,* Penguin books, 1963)

Tiziana Rocco Pompeii's Fame in Eighteenth- and Nineteenth-century Art

After the discovery of Herculaneum and Pompeii, enthusiasm for the archaeological finds around Vesuvius attracted the attention of cultured people, travellers and sovereigns for about a century, during their Grand Tour journeys abroad. The theme of the last night of Pompeii and of the flight of its inhabitants received particularly wide expression in the art and literature of the eighteenth and nineteenth centuries, both in Europe and America.

To document Pompeii's fame in art, one section of the exhibition is dedicated to eighteenth- and nineteenth-century representations of every day life, the eruption and fleeing victims. In these paintings, Pompeii becomes an emblem not only of a society that was wiped off the face of the earth in a single moment through the intervention of the gods, because of its decadence or through natural causes, but also of the rebirth of the interest in Classical culture.

In 1780, the Englishman Jacob More was the first to title a painting *Mount Vesuvius in Eruption: The Last Days of Pompeii;* after the discovery of skeletons during excavations carried out in 1812, Joseph Franque depicted the death of a woman and her children who had fallen from a cart. But the painting which appears above all to have been inspired by Bulwer-Lytton's novel, *The Last Days of Pompeii*, is Karl Bruillov's *Last Days of Pompeii*, exhibited in Saint Petersburg in 1833, in which the eruption of Vesuvius becomes the backdrop for scenes of terror and tragedy. Even though in 1767 Goethe had remarked upon the "smallness and narrowness" of Pompeii, his imagination was greatly struck by the human tragedies which unfurled at the time of the eruption in 79 A.D., as we can tell from the rapid sketches he made, now in the Kunstsammlungen in Weimar.

Neapolitan examples of this genre, which developed into a long string of Roman historical paintings amply documented by the works of Sir Lawrence Alma-Tadema, tend towards the anecdotal or sentimental. The origin of the 'neo-pompeian' genre which took off in the 1850s, goes back to Domenico Morelli and his followers, who used close knowledge of the ancient texts to reconstruct scenes of Pompeian daily life. Morelli in particular sets his scenes inside various buildings such as the baths, the *domus* and the *tabernae*. And a new technical device was now used for the faithful reproduction of archaeological sites: photography. Among Morelli's pupils are the Neapolitans Camillo Miola and Federico Maldarelli: the latter's paintings, focussing on a wide range of 'Pompeian women', met with considerable success. The Apulian painter Francesco Netti also added his contribution to this long series of 'neo-pompeian' art with his famous *Gladiator Fight During a Dinner at Pompeii*, whilst the Calabrian Enrico Salfi painted the *Amphora-seller at Pompeii*.

Federico Maldarelli,
Bedroom
of a Pompeian Lady,
1870, oil on canvas,
cm 47,5 × 71,5.
Avellino,
Amministrazione
Provinciale

Francesco Netti,
Gladiator Fight
During a Dinner
at Pompeii, *1880,*
oil on canvas,
cm 115 × 208.
Naples, Museo
e Gallerie Nazionali
di Capodimonte

Camillo Miola,
Horace in his Villa,
1877, oil on canvas,
cm 90 × 69,5.
Naples, Museo
e Gallerie Nazionali
di Capodimonte

Camillo Miola,
Virginia's Story,
1882, oil on canvas,
cm 91 × 76.
Naples, Museo
e Gallerie Nazionali
di Capodimonte

Enrico Salfi,
Amphora-seller
at Pompeii, *1883,*
oil on canvas,
cm 36 × 46,5.
Milan, Galleria d'Arte
Moderna

Federico Maldarelli,
Pompeian Women,
oil on canvas,
cm 29 × 22.
Naples, Museo
Nazionale
di San Martino

Domenico Morelli,
A Pompeian Bath,
photograph of the painting by Pietro Semplicini for the National Exhibition of 1861.
Florence, Museo di Storia della Fotografia Fratelli Alinari

Johann Wolfgang von Goethe, Flight from Pompeii, *pen and ink on paper. Weimar, Kunstsammlungen*

La morte di Plinio accaduta per l'eruzione del Vesuvio nell'anno 79
6539

Circle of Tommaso De Vivo, The Death of Pliny the Elder, *mid-nineteenth century, watercolour on paper, mm 322 × 377. Naples, Museo Nazionale di San Martino*

List of Exhibits

Herculaneum

The Villa of the Papyri
From the building
Marble statue of Hera, SAP 81595
White marble head of an Amazon, SAP 80499

The Workshop of the Gemstone Worker (*Insula Orientalis* II, 10)
From the building
Small tufa altar, SAP 76897
Marble portrait of a man, SAP 76923
Carbonised wooden bed, SAP 81597
Glass paste engraving (bust of a Maenad), MANN 155873
Cornelian engraving (Nike with palm and wreath), MANN 155874
Bone dice, SAP 76853
Four vinaigrettes in blown glass, SAP 76854
Cornelian engraving (dying Oriad), MANN 155876
Cornelian engraving (armed and seated Achilles), MANN 155877
Cornelian engraving (*Tyche*), MANN 155878
Cornelian engraving (four animals in profile), MANN 155879
Glass paste cameo (Hellenistic ruler with *kausìa*?), MANN 155881
Trinkets and necklace beads, SAP 76871
Jasper-agate engraving (lion in profile), MANN 155882
Glass paste engraving (the Niobids or Dionysus and Semele?), MANN 155883
Glass paste engraving (*Spes*), MANN 155885
Cornelian engraving (*Bonus Eventus*), MANN 155884
Amethyst engraving MANN 155886

The House of *M. Pilius Primigenius Granianus* (*Insula Orientalis* I, 1a)
From the building
Relief in cornelian, MANN 155864
Glass *simpulum*, SAP 76603
Glass goblet, SAP 76604
Bronze *signaculum*, SAP 76609
Cornelian engraving (*Athena Alkìs* or *Pròmachos*), MANN 158864
Prasium engraving (Eros or Erotes on a dolphin), MANN 168863
Small carbonised wood table, SAP 77333
Clay bottle, SAP 77339
The victims
The person in the exedra
Iron ring with cornelian engraving (scorpion), MANN 158862
The baby in the exedra
Carbonised wooden cradle, SAP 78444

The Ancient Seafront and the Arcades on the Beach at Herculaneum
From Arcade 7
Person no. 1
Glass vinaigrette, SAP 79004
Person no. 2
Gold ring, SAP 3657
Gold ring, SAP 3658
Chalcedonic agate gemstone, SAP 3824
Mass of silver coins, SAP 3681
Person no. 3
Drinking vessel in chalcedonic agate, SAP 78969
Necklace of various stones, SAP 3671
Person no. 8
Gold necklace, SAP 3661
Gold necklace with amethyst, SAP 3662
From Arcade 8
Person no. 1
Gold earring, SAP 3808
Person no. 2
Silver and gold bracelet, SAP 3698
Person no. 4
Terra-cotta lamp, SAP 3680
Gold ornament, SAP 3659
Person no. 13
Gold and silver armbands, SAP 3655–3656
Chalcedonic sardonyx gold ring, SAP 3673
Gold ring, SAP 3674
Mass of silver and bronze coins, SAP 3701
Between persons no.11 and no. 12
Gold necklace, SAP 3646
Bracelet with gold hemispheres, SAP 3647–3648
Gold knurled ring, SAP 3649
Gold ring with cornelian, SAP 3650
Gold ring with cornelian, SAP 3651
Gold ring with emerald, SAP 3652
Gold ring with amethyst, SAP 3653
Gold earrings with double pearl pendant, SAP 3654
Three containers, a ladle and a silver lid, SAP 3688–3689
Between persons no. 18 and no. 21
Hook earrings with spherical segment, SAP 3663
Gold ring with glass paste imitating chalcedony, SAP 3664
Gold ring with glass paste imitating chalcedony, SAP 3665
Mass of silver and bronze coins, SAP 3684
Between persons nos. 2, 3, 14

Bronze *aryballos*, SAP 3683
At the back and on the walls of the Arcade
Terra-cotta lamp, SAP 3676
Glass vinaigrette, SAP 3716
From Arcade 11
Skeletons nos. 14–15
Three silver teaspoons, SAP 78578
Silver bracelet, SAP 78580
Silver bracelet, SAP 78577
Silver bracelet, SAP 78581
Silver knob, SAP 78597
Bronze lamp, SAP 78635
Glass bottle, SAP 78634
Glass ointment jar, SAP 78633
Glass ointment jar, SAP 78640
Beside skeleton no. 21
Wicker basket with silver and bronze coins, SAP 78675
Assorted people
Gold earrings, SAP 78557
Gold ring with calcedonian, SAP 78547
Gold knob, SAP 78546
Gold earrings, SAP 78549
Gold and ivory ring, SAP 78554
Gold ring with emerald, SAP 78555
Gold ring, SAP 78556
Gold ring, SAP 78567
Gold ring, SAP 78565
Gold ring, SAP 78566
Gold earrings, SAP 78632
From Arcade 12
Cast of the skeletons from Arcade 12
Person no. 30
Eight aurei, SAP 78609–78610, 78937–78942
Person no. 28
Amber pendant in the form of a dog, SAP 79611
Person no. 25
Bone pin, SAP 79611
The surgeon
Small box with surgical instruments in wood, slate, bronze and iron (small slate plate, three needles and eight bronze scalpels, bronze container, a forceps and bronze probe, six cylindrical bronze cases, two scalpels in bronze, iron and wood, little box in wood and bronze), SAP 78999–79000
From the ancient seafront
Person no. 65: woman with jewels
Gold clip earrings, SAP 78356–78357
Snake-shaped armbands in gold and glass paste, SAP 78358–78359
Gold ring with scarlet garnet, SAP 78355
Gold ring with emerald, SAP 78354
Person no. 26: the soldier
Sword with iron, silver and wood sheath, SAP 79093
Dagger with iron, bone and wood sheath, SAP 79094
Silver sword-belt, SAP 79121
Silver sword-belt, SAP 79094
Punch, two chisels, a small hammer and two rings in iron, wood and bronze, SAP 79092

Oplontis

The Villa of *Lucius Crassius Tertius*
From the building
Bronze seal, SAP 71294
Strongbox in iron, bronze, copper and silver, SAP 85179
Bronze, iron and wood *olla*, SAP 72595
Bronze and iron *olla*, SAP 73938
Marble, iron and lead weight, SAP 73225
Marble, iron and lead weight, SAP 72602
Marble weight, SAP 73234
The victims
From room 10
Glass hairpin, SAP 74643
Person no. 14
Gold ring with incised bezel (palm), SAP 73417
Gold ring with smooth gold bezel, SAP 73316
Gold snake-shaped ring, SAP 73317
Gold ring with chalcedony, SAP 73313
Gold ring with engraved chalcedony (bust of Mercury), SAP 73314
Gold ring with engraved chalcedony (ox and tree), SAP 73315
Gold armband with emerald, SAP 73341
Gold armband with emerald, SAP 73312
Gold necklace with emeralds, SAP 73307
Person no. 10: the girl from Oplontis
Gold ring with engraved chalcedony (bust of Mercury), SAP 73309
Gold armband, SAP 73308
Silver hairpin, SAP 74625
Person no. 27: the owner of the villa?
Gold ring with two snake heads, SAP 73403
Gold ring with engraved bezel (insect), SAP 73404
Gold ring with smooth bezel, SAP 73402
Gold armband with engraved bezel (Eros), SAP 73401
Parts of a gold armband, SAP 73412 b–c
Gold necklace, SAP 73409
Gold chain, SAP 73410
Gold chain, SAP 73411
Gold necklace with emeralds, SAP 73412 a
Hook earrings with spherical segment, SAP 73408
Gold circle earrings, SAP 73405
Gold clip earrings with pearls, SAP 73407
175 silver denarii, SAP selezione
15 gold aurei, SAP selezione
37 silver denarii, SAP selezione
86 gold aurei, SAP selezione
Person no. 7
Cloth fragments (bag), SAP 73305
Leather bag
Fragments of leather bag, SAP 85180
Gold snake-shaped ring, SAP 73319
Gold ring with pearl, SAP 73320
Part of gold necklace, SAP 73332
Gold pendant with emeralds, SAP 73321
Gold and quartz earrings, SAP 73326
Small tangle of gold wire, SAP 73323
Small gold lace, SAP 73306

Terzigno

Villa 2
The victims
The young woman
Gold necklace with emeralds, SAP 30792
Gold necklace with pendant, SAP 30793
Necklace with gold-foil leaves, SAP 30797
Pair of gold snake-shaped armbands, SAP 30794–30795
Silver mirror, SAP 30796
Small silver amphora SAP 30798
Silver *skyphos*, SAP 30800
Silver *skyphos*, SAP 33474
Silver *situla*, SAP 33473
Bronze and silver *falera*, SAP 33475
Coin of Nero, SAP 33477
The slave family
Bronze brooch, SAP 33504

Villa 6
From the building
Frescoed wall, north side, SAP 34036
Frescoed wall, west side, SAP 34035
Frescoed wall, east side, SAP 34037

The victims
The slave group
Bronze hairpin, SAP 47149
Iron key, SAP 47138
Small bronze key, SAP 47148

Pompeii

The Villa of Diomedes
The mistress
Gold necklace with two vine-leaf pendants, SAP 24833
Cornelian engraving (horse in profile), SAP 27247

The Temple of Isis (VIII, 7, 27–28)
From the building
Fresco with Harpocrates, MANN 8975
Fresco with Io at Canopus, MANN 9558
Fresco with priest with *situla*, MANN 8918
Bronze candelabra, MANN 72192–72193
Small bronze statue of Harpocrates, MANN 5334

The Quadriporticus of the Theatres (VIII, 7, 16–17)
From the building
Bronze gladiator's helmet, MANN 5674
Bronze shoulder-guard (*galerus*), MANN 5637
Bronze shoulder-guard (*galerus*), MANN 5639
Bronze shin-guard (*ocrea*), MANN 5664
Bronze shin-guard (*ocrea*), MANN 5675
Bronze shield with copper and silver handle, MANN 5669
Iron, bone and ivory daggers, MANN 5681
The victims
The rich matron
Gold ring with engraved garnet, MANN 25123
Gold ring with engraved gemstone, MANN 25141

Vicolo degli Scheletri (VII, 13, 19)
The victims
The father
Gold ring with emerald, MANN 25230
Clip earrings with gold and pearls, MANN 24928–24929
Gold hook earring with spherical segment, MANN 25231
The mistress
Gold earrings with pendants, MANN 25232
Silver medallion representing Fortuna, MANN 25489
Silver mirror, MANN 25716
Silver teaspoon, MANN 25479
Silver teaspoon, MANN 25480
Amber statuette of putto, MANN 25813

***Caupona* V, 1, 13**
The victims
The 'jackal'
Gold ring with emerald, MANN 110805
Green bead, MANN 110825
Incised gemstone (Nike on a chariot), MANN 110823
Incised amethyst (raven, arrow, quiver), MANN 110824
Glass paste cameo (Aphrodite), MANN 110827
Cornelian scarab, MANN 110826
Gold ring with missing stone, MANN 110807
Gold ring with emerald, MANN 110806
Gold ring with double incised bezel (palm), MANN 110808
Gold ring with incised garnet (quadruped), MANN 110809
Gold ring with incised bezel (palm), MANN 110810
Gold ring with emerald, MANN 110811
Silver ring with double snake head, MANN 110814
Parts of a gold chain, MANN 110801
Parts of a silver chain, MANN 110816
Silver teaspoon, MANN 110819
Eliptical purple gemstone, MANN 110820
Incised black gemstone (white stripe), MANN 110821
Yellow gemstone, MANN 110822
Bronze signet-ring, MANN 110828
Bronze signet-ring, MANN 110829
Bar earrings in gold and pearls, MANN 110797
Gold hook earring with spherical segment, MANN 110796
Gold earring with pearl, MANN 110798
Gold bar earrings with pearls, MANN 110799
Gold ring with onyx, MANN 110802
Gold snake-shaped ring, MANN 110804
Gold ring, MANN 110803

The *caupona* of *Salvius* (VI, 14, 35–36)
From the building
Fresco with inn scenes, MANN 111482
The victims
Next to two people (the owners?) on the upper floor
Gold necklace with pendant, MANN 110921
Pair of gold bar earrings, MANN 110914
Silver ring, MANN 110918
Gold ring with quartz, MANN 110911
Gold ring with plasma stone, MANN 110909
Gold ring with emerald, MANN 110910
Gold ring with gemstone, MANN 110912
Gold ring with double bezel, MANN 110908
Gold snake-shaped ring, MANN 110922
Gold ring with double bezel, MANN 110923
Gold snake-shaped ring, MANN 110913
Pair of bracelets with gold hemispheres, MANN 110919–110920

Vicolo di Tesmus
The victims
The lady
Silver shell cup, MANN 111121
Silver shell cup, MANN 111122
Silver spoon, MANN 111125
Silver spoon, MANN 111127
Silver spoon, MANN 111128
Silver spoon, MANN 111133
Silver spoon, MANN 111134
Silver spoon, MANN 111135
Silver spoon, MANN 111136
Silver spoon, MANN 111137
Silver spoon, MANN 111139
Silver spoon, MANN 111140
Silver *oinochoe*, MANN 111124
Silver *patera*, MANN 111118
Silver *patera*, MANN 111119
Silver *simpulum*, MANN 111120
Silver mirror, MANN 111123
Lapis lazuli, MANN 111147
Lapis lazuli, MANN 111148
Gold ivy-leaf chain, MANN 111113–111114
Fragment of gold foil, MANN 111115

Gold hook earrings with spherical segment, MANN 111117
Necklace with gold and emeralds, MANN 111116

The House of *Oppius Gratus* (IX, 6, 5)
From the building
Bronze inkpot, MANN 115614
The victim
Small bracelet in bronze foil with incised figurine, MANN 115603
Small five-stranded bronze bracelet, MANN 118258
Small five-stranded bronze bracelet, MANN118259
Small five-stranded bronze bracelet, MANN 118260
Small five-stranded bronze bracelet, MANN 118261
Three-stranded bronze bracelet, MANN 118262
Bracelet with bronze hemispheres and glass paste, MANN 118270
Bracelet with bronze hemispheres and glass paste, MANN 118271
Bronze statuette of Lar, MANN 115555
Bronze statuette of Lar, MANN 115556
Bronze statuette of Mercury, MANN 115554
Silver snake-head ring, MANN 115458
Gold ring with engraved cornelian (parrot), MANN 115462

The House of the Centenary (IX, 8, 3–5)
From the building
Bronze statuette of Satyr with wineskin, MANN 111495
Fresco with Bacchus, MANN 112286
Fresco with wounded Philoctetes, MANN 120032
Mosaic *emblema* with *Gorgoneion*, MANN 112284
Small glass bottle, MANN 115148
Small glass bottle, MANN 115060
Small glass bottle, MANN 115081
The victim
Bronze key, MANN 118655
Bronze key, MANN 118656
16 bronze coins, MANN 119245
Gold pendant earrings with pearls, MANN 118712

The Nolan Gate
The victims
The couple
Bronze lamp, MANN 133320
Iron key, SAP 168
The lady
Two iron keys, SAP 284 a–b
Cylindrical silver container, SAP 285
Silver statuette-base, SAP 286
7 bronze asses, MANN 288
12 silver denarii, SAP 289
5 bronze coins, SAP 290
The girl
Gold necklace, SAP 866
Gold hook earrings with spherical segment, MANN 867
Silver spoon, MANN 136768
Imperial silver denarii, MANN 871
The girl with the jewels
Silver ring with two snake heads, SAP 15497
Silver ring with engraved bezel (palm), SAP 15498
Gold ring with emerald, SAP 23181
Iron ring with engraved sardonyx (Isis Fortuna), SAP 15532
Silver pendant, SAP 15501
Silver statuette of Isis Fortuna, SAP 15496
Silver denarius, SAP 15503
Silver denarius, SAP 15502
The armed man
Large knife with sheath in wood, silver-plated bronze and iron, SAP 17047
Wood and bronze dagger sheath, SAP 17048

The Vesuvius Gate
The first victim
Silver ring with two snake heads, SAP 819
Bronze sesterce of Vespasian, SAP 817
13 silver denarii, SAP 822
The second victim
Silver saucepan, MANN 125262
Silver teaspoon, MANN 125263
Bronze ring with two snake heads, SAP 54496
5 glass paste beads, SAP 54497
Hoard of 187 bronze coins, SAP 125267

The House of the Cryptoporticus (I, 6, 2)
From the building
Fresco with Second-style architectonic decoration, SAP 59468 (north wall), SAP 59469 a–d (south wall)
The victims
Silver *skyphos*, MANN 136791
Gold ring with garnet, MANN 137871
Knurled gold ring, MANN 137853

Via dell'Abbondanza
The victims
The fleeing man
Bronze lantern, SAP 5798
The girl
Gold ring with rock crystal, MANN 136793
Gold armband with hemispheres, MANN 136792
Gold ring with emerald, MANN 136795
Gold bar earrings with pearls, MANN 136794
Gold ring with missing gemstone, MANN 136792

The House of *Trebius Valens* (III, 2, 1)
From the building
Bronze statuette of Mercury, SAP 2276
Bronze statuette of Venus, SAP 2275
Silver spoon, SAP 2174
Silver spoon, SAP 2175
Silver *simpulum*, SAP 2173
Silver hairpin, SAP 2176
Silver hairpin, SAP 2177
Silver hairpin, SAP 2178
Iron pick-axe, SAP 2184 bis
Small iron chisel, SAP 2185 bis
Iron hatchet, SAP 2186
Iron blade, SAP 2183 bis
The victims
Person no. 1: a woman
Gold ring, MANN 138113
Gold ring, MANN 138112
Gold earring, MANN 138111
Person no. 3
Iron ring with engraved sardonyx, MANN 138114

Villa of the Mysteries
From the building
Marble statue of Livia, SAP 4400
The victims
Gold ring with smooth bezel, SAP 4487 c
Gold ring with *prasium*, SAP 4487 b
Silver-plated gold ring with *prasium*, SAP 4487 a
Gold armband with smooth bezel, SAP 4483
Gold armband with engraved bezel (palm), SAP 4492
Gold and emerald necklace, SAP 4484

The House of the Menander (I, 10, 4)
From the building
Silver *kantharos*, MANN 145513
Bronze and iron brazier, SAP 20315
Bronze dining couch, SAP 4270 a

Marble statue of Apollo,
MANN 146103
The victims
The women on the upper floor
Gold ring with emerald, SAP 4884
Gold ring with engraved cornelian (Pegasus?), SAP 4886
Bronze ring with two snake heads, SAP 4888
Denarius of *M. Scaurius*, MANN P 4887
As of Augustus, MANN P 4889
Quadrans of Augustus, MANN P 4890
The ten people in the corridor
Bronze key-ring, SAP 4802
Bronze lantern, SAP 4773
16 bronze coins, MANN P 4801
4 silver coins, MANN P 4801
6 bronze coins, MANN P 4805
The 3 people in oecus *19*
6 glass paste beads, SAP 4772

The House of the Craftsman (I, 10, 7)
From the building
Bronze compass, SAP 5547
Bronze probe, SAP 5394
Iron hatchet, SAP 18227
Iron hoe, SAP 18228
Mother-of-pearl, SAP 5340 b
Gold necklace with figured pendant (Isis Fortuna), SAP 5413
Gold hook earrings with spherical segment, SAP 5313
Gold ring with engraved garnet (dog), SAP 5415
Gold ring with engraved coral (quadruped), SAP 4314

The Large Palaestra (II, 7)
The victims
The woman in the group of 6 victims
Snake-shaped armband in silver and gold, SAP 6131
Silver ladle, SAP 6120
The doctor in the group of 8 victims
Bronze needle, SAP 6124
Bronze spatula, SAP 6127 c
Bronze spoon-shaped probe, SAP 6127 d
Bronze ear-probe, SAP 6127 e
Bronze ear-probe, SAP 6127 f
Bronze and silver instrument, SAP 6127 h
Bronze and silver instrument, SAP 6127 g
Bronze tweezers, SAP 6128 a
Bronze forceps, SAP 6128 b
Bronze and iron scalpels, SAP 6128 g–l
Small slate slab, SAP 6130
Cylindrical bronze cases, SAP 6127, 6129 a–e
The 'servant of Isis'
Silver cup with scenes of Isiac cult, MANN 6044
Silver cup with scene of Isiac cult, MANN 6045
The young athlete?
Bronze strigils, SAP 6498 a–b
The people near the swimming pool
Glass paste necklace, SAP 6395
The 18 people in the latrine
Gold ring with smooth bezel, SAP 6122
Bone hairpin, SAP 6503
Gold ring with emerald, SAP 6507
Terra-cotta lamp, SAP 6509
Glass vinaigrette, SAP 6504 a
Glass vinaigrette, SAP 6504 b
Isolated individuals
Gold and silver snake-shaped armband, SAP 6131
Sardonyx, MANN 158786
Gold ring with incised cornelian (capricorn), SAP 6121
Simple bronze ring, SAP 6123
Bronze lamp, SAP 6125
Terra-cotta lamp, SAP 6126
Gold ring with *prasium*, SAP 6043
Glass paste necklace, SAP 6502
Iron ring with lapis lazuli, SAP 6104

The *praedia* of *Julia Felix* (II, 4, 3)
From the building
Clay statue of Pittacus, SAP 20595
Fresco depicting Dionysiac cult objects, MANN 8795
Bronze cymbals, SAP 10159
The victims
Gold ring with garnet, SAP 8960
Gold ring with double bezel, SAP 8961
Gold hook earrings with spherical segment, SAP 8604 a–b
Gold ring with cornelian, SAP 8606
Gold ring with cornelian, SAP 8607
Necklace of gold, emeralds and small pearls, SAP 8608

The Harbour Gate
The victims
The lady
Gold hook earrings with spherical segment, SAP 12652
Gold crescent earrings with gemstones, SAP 12518
Gold hook earrings with pherical segment, SAP 12519
Gold hoop earrings, SAP 12524
Gold ring with emerald, SAP 12522
Gold ring with emeralds, SAP 12521
Gold ring with engraved cornelian (head of Jupiter), SAP 12520
Small statue of Mercury in silver and gold, SAP 12523

The House of the Golden Bracelet (VI, 17, 42)
From the building
Frescoed wall with central panel depicting the poet Euphorion, SAP 86075
Fresco fragment, upper portion with picture depicting a couple with maidservant, SAP 86076
Fresco fragment, upper portion with little oval picture depicting *Silenus* with a Maenad, SAP 86077
Fresco fragment, border with depiction of *kantharos* and greyhounds, SAP 86078
The victims
The woman
Gold armband with two snake heads, MANN n.i.n.
The group of 4 fugitives
Gold hook earrings with spherical segment, SAP 13313
Gold ring with garnet, SAP 13313

The House of *Julius Polybius* (IX, 13, 1–3)
From the building
Bronze statue of Apollo, as lamp stand, SAP 45180
Bronze crater, SAP 22924
The victims
The pregnant girl
Gold armband with relief bezel (the three Graces), SAP 23878
Gold armband with relief bezel (the three Graces), SAP 23879
Gold hook earrings with spherical segment, SAP 23875
Gold ring with engraved amethyst (Cupid), SAP 23877
Gold ring with engraved cornelian (athlete), SAP 23876
Silver denarius of *T. Carisius*, SAP 23916
Silver denarius of *Vibius Pansa*, SAP 23911
Silver denarius of *M. Antonius*, SAP 23910
Silver denarius of *M. Antonius*, SAP 23917
Silver denarius of *Vitellius*, SAP 23919
Silver denarius of *M. Antonius*, SAP 23909

The person in the HH triclinium
Bronze sesterces and asses,
SAP 23888 ff

Moregine, the Valiante Estate
From building A
Gold ring, MANN 113554
Gold ring, MANN 113555
Gold ring, MANN 113556
Bracelet with gold hemispheres,
MANN 114294
Gold bracelet, MANN 113542
Gold bracelet, MANN 113543
Gold bracelet, MANN 113544
Silver mirror, MANN 114296
Silver hairpin, MANN 114297
Pair of gold earrings, MANN 113545
Gold earring, MANN 113550
Gold necklace, MANN 113551
Marble trapezoid table,
MANN 114299
Pair of gold earrings, MANN 113546
Bronze needle, MANN 114422
Bronze lantern, MANN 114421
Terra-cotta statuette, MANN 114432
Unspecified place
Silver ring, MANN 114425
Bronze coin, MANN 114435
Iron ring, MANN 114430
Terra-cotta statuette, MANN 114434
The victims
The person outside building A
Pendant, MANN 113563
Engraved cornelian (warrior: *Ares*?),
MANN 114429
Cornelian, MANN 114428
The person found 4 metres from room 2, building A
Gold ring, MANN 113552
Gold ring, MANN 113553
The group of 5 people found in room 3, building A
Gold ring, MANN 113557
The group of 4 people near the north side, building A
Gold ring, MANN 113558
Gold ring, MANN 113559
Pair of gold and pearl earrings,
MANN 113548
Necklace of gold and plasma stone,
MANN 114288
Necklace of gold, mother-of-pearl
and plasma stone, MANN 113576
The group of 4 people found near the staircase, building A
Pair of gold bracelets, MANN
114317–114318
Silver bracelet, MANN 114289
Pair of silver bracelets, MANN 114290
Silver bracelet, MANN 114298
The group of 3 people near the north side, building A
Pair of earrings in gold and pearls,
MANN 113549
The person found near the north-east corner, building B
Gold ring, MANN 113560
Gold ring, MANN 113561
Pair of gold earrings, MANN 113547
Pair of gold bracelets, MANN 113541
Silver mirror, MANN 114295
Bronze signet-ring, MANN 114293

Moregine
From building A
Fresco from triclinium A, east side,
SAP 85183
Fresco from triclinium A, north side,
SAP 85182
Fresco from triclinium A, west side,
SAP 85181
Fresco from triclinium B, east side,
SAP 85186
Fresco from triclinium B, north side,
SAP 85185
Fresco from triclinium B, west side,
SAP 85184
Fresco from triclinium C, east side,
SAP 85189
Fresco from triclinium C, north side,
SAP 85188
Fresco from triclinium C, west side,
SAP 85187
From building B
Plaster with scene of sacrifice,
SAP 85193
Terra-cotta statuette of a man
in a toga, SAP 852101
The victim
The slave-girl
Simple gold circle ring, SAP 81582
Gold ring with smooth bezel,
SAP 81594
Gold ring with cornelian, SAP 81593
Tubular gold armband, SAP 81587
Tubular gold armband, SAP 81588
Gold armband with hemispheres,
SAP 81584
Gold snake-shaped armband with glass
paste, SAP 81580
Gold snake-shaped armband,
SAP 81581
Gold necklace with pendants,
SAP 81586
Gold chain, SAP 81589
Part of a gold necklace (?), SAP 81583

Bibliography

General works

G. Fiorelli, *Pompeianarum Antiquitatum Historia*, I–III, Napoli 1860–1864.
R. Siviero, *Gli Ori e le Ambre del Museo Nazionale di Napoli,* Firenze 1954.
R. Étienne, *La vita quotidiana a Pompei,* Milano 1973.
E. La Rocca, M. and A. de Vos, *Guida archeologica di Pompei*, Milano 1976.
A. and M. de Vos, *Pompei Ercolano Stabia, Guida archeologica*, Roma–Bari 1982.
A. Maiuri, *Pompei ed Ercolano fra case e abitanti*, Firenze 1983.
U. Pannuti, *Catalogo della Collezione Glittica*, I–II, Roma 1983–1994.
L. Pirzio Biroli Stefanelli, *L'Argento dei Romani. Vasellame da tavola e d'apparato*, Roma 1991.
L. Pirzio Biroli Stefanelli, *L'Oro dei Romani*, Roma 1992.
A. d'Ambrosio, E. De Carolis, *I monili dall'area vesuviana*, Roma 1997.
E. De Carolis, G. Patricelli, A. Ciarallo, "Rinvenimenti di corpi nell'area urbana di Pompei", in *Rivista di Studi Pompeiani*, IX, 1998, Roma 1999.
A. d'Ambrosio, *La bellezza femminile a Pompei*, Roma 2001.

Reference works based on location

Ercolano

The Villa of the Papyri
M.R. Woicik, *La Villa dei Papiri ad Ercolano*, Roma 1986.
A. De Simone, "Ercolano 1992–1997. La Villa dei Papiri e lo scavo della città", *Cronache Ercolanesi*, 28, 1998, pp. 3–63.

The House of M. Pilius Primigenius Granianus
A. Maiuri, *Ercolano. I Nuovi Scavi*, I, Roma 1958.

The ancient seafront and the Arcades at Herculaneum

M. Pagano, "Attività della Soprintendenza. Ercolano", *Rivista di Studi Pompeiani*, III, 1989, pp. 243 ff.
E. De Carolis, "Lo scavo dei fornici 7 e 8 sulla marina di Ercolano", *Rivista di Studi Pompeiani*, VI, 1993–1994, pp. 167–186.
L. Capasso, *I fuggiaschi di Ercolano. Paleobiologia delle vittime dell'eruzione vesuviana del 79 d.C.*, Roma 2001.
Vesuvio 79 A.D. Vita e morte ad Ercolano, edited by P.P. Petrone and F. Fedele, Napoli 2002.

Oplontis

A. de Franciscis, "Oplonti, Torre Annunziata", *Fasti Archeologici*, 18–19 (1963–1964), 1968, p. 524, no. 7420.
A. Lagi De Caro, "Villa B", *Pompei Herculaneum Stabiae*, 1, 1983, pp. 369–375.
A. d'Ambrosio, *Gli ori di Oplontis. Gioielli romani dal suburbio pompeiano*, Napoli 1987.

Terzigno

Villa 2
C. Cicirelli, "Comune di Terzigno. Località Boccia al Mauro, proprietà Cava Ranieri", *Rivista di Studi Pompeiani*, III, 1989, pp. 249–253.
C. Cicirelli, "Pompei – Suburbio. Comune di Terzigno. Località Boccia al Mauro, proprietà Cava Ranieri", *Rivista di Studi Pompeiani*, V (1991–1992), 1994, pp. 208–211.
C. Cicirelli, "La Villa di Terzigno", in *Casali di ieri Casali di oggi*, Napoli 2000.

Villa 6
C. Cicirelli, "Comune di Terzigno. Località Boccia al Mauro, Cava Ranieri", *Riv-*

ista di Studi Pompeiani,VI, 1993–1994, pp. 233–238.
C. Cicirelli, "Comune di Terzigno. Località Boccia al Mauro", *Rivista di Studi Pompeiani*,VII, 1995–1996, pp. 183–185.
C. Cicirelli, "Comune di Terzigno. Località Boccia al Mauro", *Rivista di Studi Pompeiani*,VIII, 1997, pp. 175–179.

POMPEII

The Villa of Diomedes
T.H.M. Fontaine, "Die Villa des Diomedes", *Mitt.DAI*,V.22.1, 1991, pp. 31–33.

The Temple of Isis
V. Tran Tam Tinh, *Essai sur le culte d'Isis à Pompei*, Paris 1964.
Alla ricerca di Iside: analisi, studi, restauri dell'Iseo Pompeiano nel Museo di Napoli, Roma 1992.
N. Blanc, H. Eriston, M. Frinker, "A fundamento restituit? Réfection dans le temple d'Isis à Pompei", *Revue Archeologique*, 2, 2000, pp. 227–309.

The Quadriporticus of the Theatres
G. Minervini, "Studii Pompeiani – Caserma de' Gladiatori", *Bullettino Archeologico Neapolitano*, n.s. 8, 1860, pp. 41–48.
Sangue e arena, exh. cat. edited by A. La Regina, Milano 2001.

Caupona V, 1, 13
M. della Corte, *Case ed abitanti di Pompei*, Napoli 1965, pp. 97–98.
J.E. Packer, "Inns at Pompeii: a Short Survey", *Cronache Pompeiane* IV, 1978, pp. 5–53.

The Caupona of Salvius
F. Zevi, "L'Art 'populaire'", in *La peinture de Pompéi*, I, pp. 305–312, Paris 1993.
I. Brigantini, in *Pompei. Pitture e Mosaici*, Istituto dell'Enciclopedia Italiana di G. Treccani, V, 1994, pp. 366 ff.

The House of Oppius Gratus (IX, 6, 5)
A. Sogliano, "Pompei", *Notizie degli Scavi di Antichità*, 1878, pp. 322–324, 371–373.
A. Sogliano, "Pompei", *Notizie degli Scavi di Antichità*, 1879, pp. 19–20, 45.
M. della Corte, *Case ed abitanti di Pompei*, Napoli 1965, pp. 163–164.

The House of the Centenary (IX, 8, 3–5)
A. Sogliano, "Pompei", *Notizie degli Scavi di Antichità*, 1879, pp. 143–153, 280–287.
A. Sogliano, "Pompei", *Notizie degli Scavi di Antichità*, 1880, pp. 97–101.
D. Scagliarini Corlàita, Antonella Coralini (eds.), *L'Alma Mater a Pompei. L'Insula del Centenario*, Bologna 2000.

The Nolan Gate
G. Spano, "Pompei. Scavi fuori Porta di Nola", *Notizie degli Scavi di Antichità*, 1910, pp. 385–399.
S. De Caro, "Scavi nell'area fuori Porta Nola a Pompei", *Cronache Pompeiane*, 5, 1979 (Napoli 1982), pp. 61–101.

The Vesuvius Gate
A. Sogliano, "Pompei. Relazione degli scavi fatti durante il mese di ottobre", *Notizie degli Scavi di Antichità*, 1900, pp. 500–501.

The House of the Cryptoporticus
Notizie degli Scavi di Antichità, 1914, pp. 204–206, 228, 260–263, 365.
Pompeii. Picta Fragmenta, exh. cat., Torino 1997.

Via dell'Abbondanza
V. Spinazzola, "Pompei. Continuazione dello scavo su via dell'Abbondanza. Rinvenimenti di due scheletri e di oggetti preziosi", *Notizie degli Scavi di Antichità*, 1914, pp. 205–208.

The Villa of the Mysteries
A. Maiuri, *La villa dei Misteri*, 2 vols., Roma 1931.
P. Veyne, "La fresque dite des Mystères à Pompèi", in P. Veyne, F. Lissarague, F. Frontisi-Ducroux, *Les mystères du gynécée*, Paris 1998, pp. 15–153.
M.P. Guidobaldi, C. Cicirelli, *Pavimenti e mosaici nella Villa dei Misteri di Pompei*, Napoli 2000.

The House of the Menander (I, 10, 4)
A. Maiuri, *La Casa del Menandro e il suo tesoro di argenteria*, Roma 1933.
R. Ling, "The Insula of the Menander at Pompeii: Interim Report", *The Antiquaries Journal*, LXIII, 1983.

The House of the Craftsman (I, 10, 7)
O. Elia, "Pompei. Relazione sullo scavo dell'Insula X della Regio I", *Notizie degli Scavi di Antichità*, 1934, pp. 264–344.

The Large Palaestra
Notizie Scavi di Antichità, 1939, pp. 165–238.
A. Maiuri, *Pompei ed Ercolano fra case ed abitanti*, Firenze 1983.

The Praedia of Julia Felix
A. Maiuri, *Pompei ed Ercolano fra case e abitanti*, Firenze 1983, pp. 51–54.

The Harbour Gate
L. Jacobelli, *Le Pitture erotiche delle Terme Suburbane di Pompei*, Roma 1995, pp. 13–24.

The House of the Golden Bracelet
Pompeii. Picta Fragmenta, exh. cat., Torino 1997, pp. 96, 130–133, 166–167.
Pitture nella reggia dalle città sepolte, exh. cat., Napoli 1999, pp. 70, 71, 78–79, 92.

The House of Julius Polybius
A. de Franciscis, "La Casa di C. Iulius Polybius", *Rivista di Studi Pompeiani*, II, 1988 pp. 15–36.
F. Zevi, "La casa di Giulio Polibio", in *Abitare sotto il Vesuvio*, exh. cat., Ferrara 1996, pp. 73–85.
La Casa di Giulio Polibio. Studi interdisciplinari, edited by A.M. Ciarallo and E. De Carolis, Pompei 2001.

Moregine: the Building of the Triclinia
Pompei le stanze dipinte, exh. cat. edited by P.G. Guzzo and M. Mastroroberto, Milano 2002.

This book was printed on behalf of Mondadori Electa S.p.A.
at Martellago Mondadori Printing S.p.A.,
Via Castellana 98, Martellago (Venice) in the year 2003